Medieval & Renaissance Miniatures
FROM THE NATIONAL GALLERY OF ART

Medieval & Renaissance Miniatures
FROM THE NATIONAL GALLERY OF ART

Compiled by
CARRA FERGUSON
DAVID S. STEVENS SCHAFF
GARY VIKAN

Under the direction of
CARL NORDENFALK

Edited by
GARY VIKAN

NATIONAL GALLERY OF ART
WASHINGTON   1975

*This catalogue was produced by
the Editor's Office, National Gallery of Art, Washington.
Printed by the Meriden Gravure Company, Meriden, Connecticut.
Set in Linotype and Monotype Janson
by the Monotype Composition Company, Inc., Baltimore, Maryland.
The text paper is 80 pound Mohawk Superfine, and the
cover 80 pound Mohawk Superfine.
Designed by Frances P. Smyth*

Library of Congress Cataloging in Publication Data
United States.   National Gallery of Art.
    Medieval and Renaissance miniatures from the National
Gallery of Art.

    Includes bibliographical references.
    1.   Illumination of books and manuscripts, Medieval—
Catalogs.   2.   Illumination of books and manuscripts,
Renaissance—Catalogs.   3.   Illumination of books and
manuscripts—Washington, D. C.—Catalogs.   4.   United
States.   National Gallery of Art.   I.   Nordenfalk, Carl
Adam Johan, 1907-   II.   Title.
ND2920.U54   1975   016.09   74-28397

Exhibition dates at the National Gallery of Art: January 26 – June 1, 19

Cover: Catalogue no. 18

Contents

Foreword

Once more the National Gallery of Art is in the happy position of showing its gratitude to Lessing J. Rosenwald by publishing a scholarly catalogue of a portion of his collection, all of which he has generously given to the nation. After *Fifteenth Century Woodcuts and Metal Cuts* (1965), *Fifteenth Century Engravings of Northern Europe* (1967), and *Prints of the Italian Renaissance* (1973), we have now come to the publication of single leaves and cuttings from medieval and Renaissance illuminated manuscripts, which form a numerically smaller but artistically important part of Mr. Rosenwald's donation. The present exhibition constitutes the first complete showing of that collection; not since 1950 have any of these miniatures been displayed at the National Gallery.

Whereas Mr. Rosenwald has presented to the Library of Congress the complete manuscripts he has acquired over a period of years, he found it appropriate to enrich the National Gallery with his collection of single leaves and cuttings. An extraordinary opportunity is thus afforded specialist and non-specialist alike to examine a cross-section of western miniature styles and book types: from a Romanesque Giant Bible leaf to a tiny illumination from a Renaissance Book of Hours; from central Italy and southern Spain to the Loire Valley, northern Germany and Bohemia. The manuscripts serve also as a valuable introduction to the history of prints and drawings—a history which, in fact, begins about the same time that book illumination draws toward its end.

For the preparation of this catalogue, the National Gallery has had the advantage of the knowledge and enthusiasm of Dr. Carl Nordenfalk during the time he served as Kress Professor at the Gallery in 1972–1973. Under his direction the catalogue was compiled by three Kress Fellows—Carra Ferguson, David Schaff and, as chief editor, Gary Vikan.

In dealing with materials as highly diversified as that of the Rosenwald collection of miniatures, the authors of the catalogue have solicited the advice and opinions of some of the leading scholars in this particular field of knowledge. The authors have met with warm cooperation from every side, and it therefore gives me great pleasure to thank, on behalf of the National Gallery, and Dr. Nordenfalk and his collaborators, a number of distinguished scholars: J. J. G. Alexander, François Avril, Hans Belting, Carlo Bertelli, Knut Berg, Miklòs Boskovitz, François Bucher, Christopher Clarkson, Alessandro Contini-Bonacossi, Gino Corti, Peter Dreyer, Marvin Eisenberg, Friedrich Gorissen, Rosalie Green, Edith Kirsch, Stephen Kuttner, Mirella Levi D'Ancona, Millard Meiss, H. W. van Os, Otto Pächt, John Plummer, Gisela Plotzek-Wederhake, Gerhard Schmidt, Harvey Stahl, M. Alison Stones, Hanns Swarzenski, Ilaria Toesca, and David Wilkins.

It is, primarily, to Professor Nordenfalk himself, and to the donor, Lessing J. Rosenwald, that we owe this exhibition. May it provide our audience here at the Gallery, as well as readers of this catalogue for years to come, a sense of the creativity of the medieval mind, and of the eye and erudition of all those who have helped illuminate this precious heritage in our own day.

J. CARTER BROWN *Director*

Preface

A great many examples of early manuscript illustration have survived. Of these a large number are either crude or have little artistic merit. The fine ones that have come down to us have often suffered the injuries of time. Pristine examples of this great art of the past are relatively rare. The selection of prime specimens requires qualifications possessed by few specialists in this field. I believe the examples in this exhibition are of very high quality. As a collector, I cannot claim any credit, as I have never studied the subject sufficiently to consider myself an authority.

Almost all the miniatures exhibited were purchased from Dr. Erwin Rosenthal. During the war years he was living in Oakland, California and it was at that time I came to know him. It was while I was on a visit to California that he brought many of them to my attention. I was so impressed by their inherent beauty and their splendid preservation, as well as by Dr. Rosenthal's great knowledge of the subject, that I bought many of them. Dr. Rosenthal, now living in Lugano, has made a lifetime study of manuscript illumination and continues to do so. This exhibition is therefore a testament to his taste and erudition.

As will be noted, all but four of the miniatures in the catalogue have a direct connection with a liturgical text. Some are the capital letters of the first word immediately following. This, however, does not occur in all cases. In several instances the scribes may have felt it necessary to enliven the text with a picture—regardless of any scriptural connection. One case that comes to mind is a marginal illustration in a thirteenth-century Bible of a "centaurette" nursing her offspring.

I hope that those who look at these reminders of the past will derive from them as much enjoyment as they have given me for many years.

LESSING J. ROSENWALD

COLORPLATE I, Catalogue 3, *Leaf from a Choir Book*

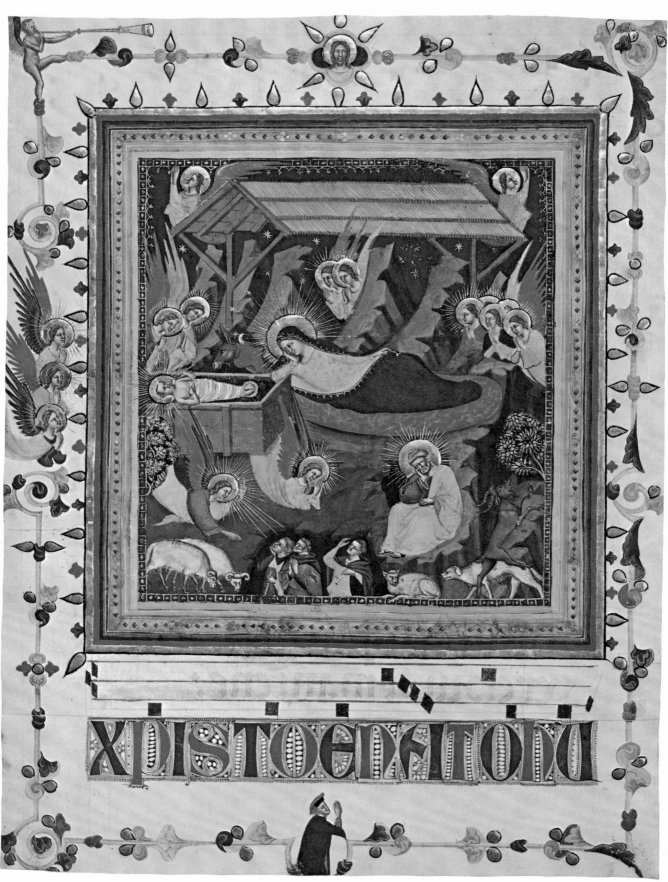

COLORPLATE II, Catalogue 7, *Leaf from a Choir Book*

COLORPLATE III, Catalogue 13, *Initial E from a Choir Book* (1:1)

COLORPLATE IV, Catalogue *15*, *Leaf from the* Novella
of Johannes Andreae (detail, 1:1)

COLORPLATE V, Catalogue 18, *Initial I from a Choir Book* (1:1)

COLORPLATE VI, Catalogue 20, *Leaf from a Choir Book* (detail)

COLORPLATE X, Catalogue 46B,
Initial T from a Choir Book (1:1)

COLORPLATE VIII, Catalogue 38, *Leaf from a Book of Hours* (1:1)

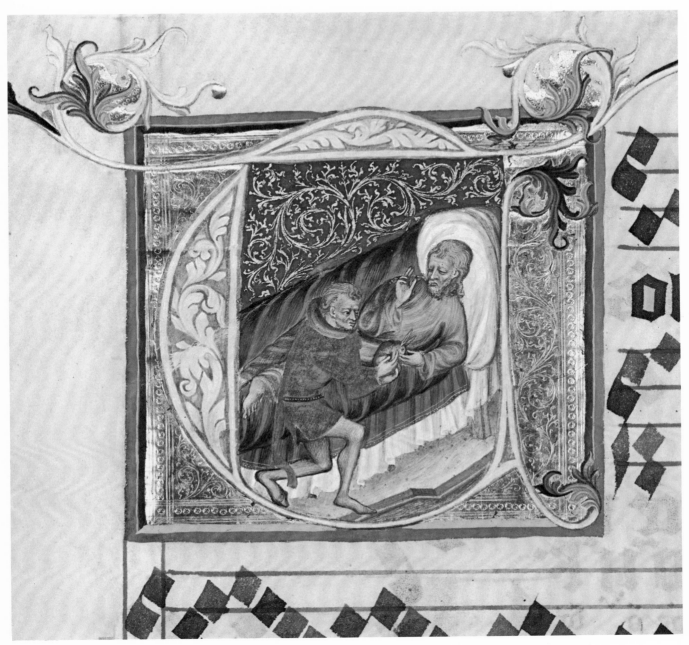

COLORPLATE IX, Catalogue 41B, *Leaf from a Choir Book* (detail, 1:1)

COLORPLATE VII, Catalogue 33, *Leaf from a Psalter*

Medieval Book Illumination
as seen in the collection of the National Gallery of Art

The oldest miniature in the collection of single leaves and cuttings from illuminated manuscripts given by Lessing J. Rosenwald to the National Gallery of Art belongs to the beginning of the Romanesque period, not long before 1100 A.D. At that time Western book illumination was a firmly established branch of medieval art. The great liturgical manuscripts of the Hiberno-Saxon, Carolingian, Ottonian, and Late Anglo-Saxon schools had already come into being—codices in which book illumination was raised to an art sui generis, distinguished by a fusion of calligraphy, ornament, and pictures into an organic whole.

For Romanesque artists, such models were at hand in practically every monastery, and their importance was distinguished not only by their sumptuousness, but also by their connection with the important patrons who had commissioned them. Still, Romanesque illumination is characterized more by its independence than by its continuation of the great trends of the past. Rejecting the classicizing tendencies of the Carolingian, Anglo-Saxon, and Ottonian schools, but sensitive to the lesson of Byzantine art, the Romanesque miniaturists developed an art based on compact form and plastic values. In so doing, they joined the trend toward uniformity that seized Western art in all media in the course of the twelfth century.

Nowhere does the break with the deluxe production of the pre-Romanesque schools appear more strikingly than in the manuscripts made in Rome in the period following the Pope's call for a new concord of the Christian church against secular power. A good example of their non-illusionistic style is provided by the first item of this catalogue, the only surviving fragment of one of those Giant Bibles by which the papal curia intended to establish its own revised version of the Holy Writ. Here, the unknown painter has freely mingled both lettering and images within the same frame, using a seemingly undeveloped and flat figure style. Supremely indifferent to the refinements of the court artists of the earlier period, he seems to revive the primitivism that had characterized certain schools of the pre-Carolingian past.

At a later stage in the development of these large Italian Bibles, the Tuscan merchant cities joined forces with the Umbrian and Roman schools. The "geometric" initials now were enriched with rinceaux fillings, whereas the figures, inserted on the top of the letter or enclosed in the opening of the initial itself, appear more organically structured. Yet, in two bifolios from a Giant Bible, possibly made in Siena in the last quarter of the twelfth century (cat. 2), primitivism is still a conspicuous ingredient of the figure style as well as the spatial organization. And in a distant corner of Spain—if indeed that is where the fragment with the mysterious representation of nine Apostles seated with bare legs was painted (cat. 28)—a provincial off-shoot of this same primitive trend still asserted its vital force late in the twelfth century.

The new homogeneity of the Romanesque style did not exclude certain variations of a regional or temporal nature. The artistic traditions established in Ottonian and late Anglo-Saxon illumination, for example, still appear only partly amalgamated into the Romanesque style in the early twelfth-century Majestas Domini and Crucifixion on a leaf from a northern French mass book (cat. 26). Eventually they emerged, however, into a fully developed Romanesque figure style, as in the fragment of a German Sacramentary, which shows four standing saints (cat. 29B). Their blocklike bodies remind us that in this period, monumental sculpture in stone, using the same pillar-shaped figures, had again become part of the building program of the churches.

In the treatment of the human figure, Romanesque artists gradually learned to detach the drapery from the body, thereby giving a more accurate description of the softness and tactile character of the cloth. Compared to the shell-like treatment of the garments in the Lambach miniature (cat. 27), the drapery of the prophet forming the vertical stem of the initial P in a fragment from an early thirteenth-century Bible now in Halberstadt (cat. 31) assumes an agitated movement entirely of its own. Here and in the miniatures from two later Saxon Psalters (cats. 33–34) of the same century, the expressionism so often inherent in German art has led to a wrinkling of the loosened garments into a multitude of sharply broken folds. The *Zackenstil*, as this expressionism has been called, owes its existence to the artist's desire to force the liveliness of his design to the utmost. As is often the case with expressionist trends, this style culminated in a rather fossilized mannerism, as can be seen in another leaf from a similar Psalter (cat. 32).

Besides the figurative miniatures, the initials were a prominent feature in the decoration of the medieval book. The Vere dignum monogram, which once formed part of a German Sacramentary leaf (cat. 29A), may be taken as a clear example of a fully developed medieval initial with its spiral rinceaux (an ornamental motif of tendrils and branching scrollwork) filling the interstices of the letters in tightly wound curves. During the first half millenium in the history of the initial, there is a significant development in the relationship between the letter and its scrollwork filling. In the late antique period, classical rinceaux had been attached to an initial in a graphically simplified form, as a flourish or a linear padding of the letter's stem, without interfering with its alphabetic form. In Carolingian initials, the letter still asserts itself as the dominant element, whereas in those of the Ottonion period, the letter and its rinceaux filling are in perfect equilibrium. During the Romanesque period, however, the rinceaux begins to dominate to the extent of seemingly overwhelming the letter, as in the sketch of a grand initial A found on the back of a leaf detached from a commentary of Bede on the Apocalypse and probably designed by an Austrian artist in Lambach some decades later than the book itself (cat. 27). Having reached this stage, the development could be pushed no further. It only remained for the rinceaux to extend into the margins of the page, as happened in the course of the thirteenth century under the leadership of French Gothic book decorators.

The Renaissance schools of the Carolingian and Ottonian periods, as well as the insular schools which preceded them, had as their most

important task the production of precious Gospel books. In its break with immediate traditions, however, Romanesque book illumination is characterized by a return to the Merovingian preference for patristic manuscripts and Sacramentaries. Not by chance do the fragments of twelfth-century miniatures in the Rosenwald Collection, apart from the Italian Bible leaves, represent parts of mass books or exegetical commentaries.

In the twelfth century another type of richly decorated manuscript, the Psalter, rose to a position of prominence where it was to remain throughout the early Gothic period. Psalters began at this time to be distinguished by a set of full–page miniatures showing scenes from the life of David and from that of Christ. These scenes served as a kind of devotional image, which the owner of the book could contemplate while reciting prayers. Separated from the text, these full–page miniatures show few specifically bookish features, bringing the art of illumination close to that of panel painting, which emerged in the thirteenth century as an important new branch of art. Several miniatures in this collection (cats. 32–34) were part of such Psalters, which were made in many cases for pious women of rank. In some of these prefatory images the devotion of the worshiper and the sanctity of his prayer and praise is reflected in a miniature enactment of the worship experience. Thus, in the leaf with the Crucifixion taken from a northern French or Flemish prayer book of the early thirteenth century, there are two kneeling nuns in the lower margin, holding up devotional scrolls to Christ on the cross (cat. 38). Similarly, in a leaf from a Cologne Gradual (cat. 36) and in two leaves from Florentine Laudaria (cat. 7–8) of the fourteenth century, those who paid for the execution of the manuscripts are shown kneeling in the margins.

With the transition to the Gothic, the stylistic unity of European art came to an end, and the northern countries and Italy went their several ways. Under the impact of stained glass designs, book illuminators in France and England adopted the elegantly swinging lines, elongated bodies, and graphic formulas for the rendering of features, that are typical of Gothic art. All of these elements may be seen in the Crucifixion miniature just mentioned, as well as in the historiated initials of two Rosenwald leaves from a late thirteenth-century Bible (cat. 37 A, B). In Italy, on the other hand, the Byzantine influence, which had played so great a part initially in the formation of the Romanesque style, remained an active force and a reminder of the classical traditions from which Italian book illumination ultimately grew. With the continued Byzantine influence, spatial and plastic values received increased attention, and under the leadership of Giotto, panel and mural painting reached a new peak of expressiveness and grandeur. Although in the decades before and after 1300 the art of book illumination could not escape being influenced, and even somewhat overshadowed, by these two other branches of painting, the fourteenth century is nonetheless distinguished as a great period in the history of Italian book decoration as well. After all, Dante in his *Divina Commedia* found it proper to pay homage not only to Cimabue and Giotto, but also to the two miniaturists, Oderisi da Gubbio and Franco Bolognese, whose work unfortunately still remains unidentified. Not just by accident, it is in its splendid set of Italian miniatures of this period that the Rosenwald Collection has its greatest strength.

The popular assumption that the derivation of the word *miniature* is from the Latin *minor* is due to a false etymology. In reality, the word comes from *minium,* meaning the red color used for rubrics—the most elementary way of breaking the monotony of the monochromatic black or brown script, first used by the scribes of antiquity. Yet, the popular interpretation of the word brings an essential character of the art of book decoration to light, since the reduced areas with which the illuminator worked could not but affect his style. If size was a drawback, or at least a limitation, the medieval miniaturists, particularly those of the northern schools, were often able to make a virtue of it, and this ability, more than anything else, explains the generally high standard of book illumination in the finest specimens of the Gothic style.

The Italian miniaturists, on the other hand, were more at ease when allowed to work with large volumes—a preference already evidenced in the early Romanesque period by their Giant Bibles and Homiliaries. A new opportunity to work in a quasi-monumental scale was given them by the development of church music in the course of the thirteenth century. Church music, which since the time of Gregory the Great, and earlier, had been an important part of the Christian service, now assumed even more elaborate forms and led to the creation of the large–size corale, designed to rest on a high lectern in the choir, visible to all the singers standing in a half-circle in front of it (fig. 46B). If practical considerations were the main reason for the giant size of these choir books, it was certainly also welcomed by the painters employed for their decoration. The leaves, often measuring up to half a meter or more in height, enabled the illuminators to paint historiated initials larger in scale than anything that had been done before; in fact, these images were not much smaller than the images on the predellas of the altars. In these initials, the tendency towards monumentality is particularly striking when, as is often the case with the corali illuminated by Nicolò da Bologna, the figures are rendered in half-length (cat. 16). Thus in their predilection for large–scale effects, Italian book illuminators sometimes almost transcended the natural limits of the craft itself.

Giant choir books remained popular in Italy throughout the fifteenth century, as documented by several items in the Rosenwald Collection (cats. 20, 24). Most of them were written and illuminated in the northern parts of the country. The school of Milan attracted, under the patronage of the art-loving Visconti, several outstanding talents. One of them, Belbello da Pavia, is probably partially responsible for one of the largest and most splendid leaves in the collection (cat. 20). Observe the half–naturalistic treatment of the flowers in the border, so distinctly different from the conventional vine and acanthus motives then commonly used. Still, during the third quarter of the century, an artist close to the Ferrarese master Cosimo Tura painted an initial showing the stigmatization of Saint Francis in a manner not too different from that of his predecessors (cat. 23). In spite of the rendering of the landscape in perspective, this latter example still adheres to the trecento tradition, in which artists were more concerned with relating the miniature to its surface area than they were with illusionistic effects. As to the placement of the decoration in relation to the text, the trecento tradition did not give way until it was displaced by the reform of the written and printed book sponsored by the humanists.

In the fifteenth century large choir books became popular in Spain as well; in fact, the largest ones ever executed are those filling the showcases in the sacristies of Spanish cathedrals. The set of thirteen cuttings attributed to an illuminator in Seville called "The Master of the Cypresses" are the remnants of such a grand choir book (cat. 46 A–M). This artist was no doubt acquainted with the artistic circle around Lorenzo Monaco, from which two representative initials are in the collection (cats. 11, 13). But there is also, as often occurs in Spanish paintings of the fifteenth century, a northern element in this artist's style, with his concern for furniture and still-life detail.

North of the Alps, large choir books came into use in Bohemia and Austria during the late fourteenth and early fifteenth centuries, reflecting the influence of the Italian preference for large-size manuscripts. The Italian influence also affected the figure style of this northern school that flourished under the protection of the Luxembourg rulers. The Rosenwald Collection has a substantial set of leaves and cuttings taken from such choir books (cats. 41 A–C, 42–44). Their historiated initials differ, however, from the Italian prototypes by using a smaller figure scale, and there is more Gothic buoyancy than Italian solidity in the draperies of the figures.

Besides icon and wall painting, there was another branch of art with which book illumination had a special affinity—that of the goldsmiths. The close relationship between the two crafts goes back to the late antique period, when gold was first used for writing and when sumptuous manuscripts were first provided with covers coated with gold, and it remained effective throughout the Middle Ages. More than one miniaturist may have been trained in both crafts; a case in point is Matteo di Ser Cambio of Perugia, who is represented in the collection by two cuttings from a *Matricola* and whom we know was also active as a goldsmith (cat. 9 A, B). Both the book decorator and the goldsmith had to comply with the special conditions created by a small working surface, and precision of detail and perfect skill in handling complicated patterns were in both cases highly appreciated merits.

There were, of course, among the ecclesiastical sponsors those who disapproved of the use of gold and other precious materials. No one acquainted with the austerity of the eleventh-century Gregorian reform will be surprised that the Giant Bibles mentioned above carry no gold in the fillets of their initials and frameworks. A similar belief, rather than a lack of means, might explain why the Romanesque Vere dignum initial of the Sacramentary probably written at Corvey (cat. 29A) was drawn in minium only. Yet, the tradition of gold and gilding in connection with precious books could not be eradicated by a formal ecclesiastical ban; for the opposite view could also be held—that the illuminator using precious material paid an appropriate homage to the Holy Writ. The Gothic period saw an increase rather than a decrease in the use of gold in manuscripts, and the artist delighted particularly in the shining effect of gold leaf applied over a gesso ground—a process which allowed the gold to be burnished.

Besides ecclesiastical institutions, there were secular benefactors and collectors supporting the production of sumptuous manuscripts, and with them it was the purse rather than any pangs of conscience that

put a limit to the use of costly materials. Medieval illumination would not be the splendid chapter in the history of art that it is, had it not been supported by princes with unlimited means and a taste for grandeur and refinement. The oldest documented manuscript written in gold on purple was made in the fourth century for Constantine the Great. He begins the splendid line of royal bibliophiles, among whom Charles the Bald, Henry II of Germany, Saint Louis, Wenceslaus of Bohemia, Charles V of France and his brethren, Philip the Good of Burgundy, Ferdinand of Aragon, and Matthias Corvinus of Hungary are rightly famous. The Rosenwald Collection contains at least one leaf that might have been part of a Book of Hours begun at the order of the most distinguished of all these lovers and connoisseurs of precious books, Jean, Duc de Berry (cat. 39).

The influence of the secular patron and the growing importance of the laity could not fail to affect the development of book decoration, particularly during the late Middle Ages. Prayer books for the private use of noble ladies and other high-ranking members of society became more numerous and often more richly decorated than the books used at mass. The four leaves with portraits of the Evangelists in the Rosenwald Collection (cat. 40 A–D) come from such a Book of Hours, which is likely to have had at least a dozen or more miniatures of the same sort. For secular readers the Bible and the lives of the saints were translated, and a new vernacular literature dealing with secular matters arose and demanded the services of the miniaturists. The heroes of classical antiquity and those of the early Middle Ages took on living form in the illustrated editions of epics and chronicles, with their heroes and heroines always appearing as contemporary dukes and damsels. Hector and Achilles in the miniature cut from a fifteenth-century *Histoire ancienne jusq'à César* (cat. 47) exemplify this style. The coats-of-arms as well as other heraldic devices of the patrons asserted themselves in both an open and a more sophisticated manner. And in the margins, the droleries, with their pleasing yet disquieting images of birds and rabbits, hunters and musicians, animals dressed as men and men in the guise of animals, introduce a frankly secular note, even when the text does not call for it. In the Rosenwald Collection, the leaf from a Cologne Gradual (cat. 36) provides an early example of this trend, which transformed the pages, even in books of private devotion, into "light reading" of a more or less irreverent nature.

As the art of book decoration lost its ecclesiastical foundation, the conditions for its pursuit also changed fundamentally. In the early Middle Ages, manuscripts were illuminated in monasteries for the praise and honor of God, but later, as leading miniaturists began to work within the milieu of the universities and feudal courts, the Church lost its monopoly on the production of costly books. Students of law and medicine could, if they had wealthy parents, have their textbooks richly illustrated and decorated, as was the case with the page (cat. 15) in the Rosenwald Collection from the Decretals of Gregory IX illuminated by Nicolò da Bologna.

The cells of monks and nuns were not the natural place of manufacture for these secular texts, nor for the vernacular writings. A new class of craftsman came into being, who did not work for the eternal salvation of his soul but for money to support wife and family. Even books of religious and theological content were often produced

by such professional scribes and illuminators. At least as far back as the twelfth century, Italian artists specializing in illumination had been for hire in the merchant cities. Beginning with the Gothic period, we find the names of scribes and book illuminators in documents and in tax registers, from which some insight may be gained as to how the work was distributed. During the earlier centuries, scribe and illuminator were often the same person. From the thirteenth century onward, however, when commercial production started in earnest, a division of labor became the rule, not only between scribe and illuminator but also among all the members of a workshop. On the same page, one person may have produced the text, another the rubrics, a third the marginal decoration, a fourth the setting in the miniature, and a fifth, generally the master of the atelier, the figures. It is also striking how often artists of quite different education and talent can be seen working side by side in the same book. Not only in monasteries but also in the secular workshops, women were employed as scribes and as miniaturists. Christine de Pisan, the Italian "bluestocking" at the court of the Valois king in Paris around 1400, mentions a lady by the name of Anastasie who was so clever in painting rinceaux and checkered backgrounds that no one equalled her in the whole of Paris. However, with such specialization came one of the greatest dangers in art: routine. Witness the numerous late fifteenth-century books of hours, the miniatures of which were practically mass produced.

Modern scholarship has shown that book illumination around 1400 played a seminal role in the development of European painting. Miniaturists fostered a more wholehearted acceptance of nature, as seen with unprejudiced eyes, than what their colleagues, working in a more grand style, mastered. Through the new preoccupation with illusionistic effects, however, book illumination also sowed the seeds of its own dissolution. Perspective, which enables us to look into the picture as through a window, threatened to break the organic unity of the flat book page. For the leading masters of the fifteenth and early sixteenth centuries, an increasingly sophisticated manipulation of this intrinsic conflict was a mark of the artist's skill and creativity.

The Rosenwald Collection does not contain any typical example of the trompe-l'œil effects, which were achieved in different ways in both Italian and Netherlandish manuscripts of the late medieval and early Renaissance period. Had the whole page to which it originally belonged been preserved, the little miniature by Simon Bening (cat. 49) might have shown the use of those leaves and flowers scattered over the margin, as if they were real, that were typical for the Ghent-Bruges school of his day. Painted as late as 1530, this piece stands at the end of the history of an art which, by that time, had exhausted its means of regeneration, but still managed to maintain a level of quality comparable to some of the finest miniatures of its kind—a worthy final vignette to the collection of which it forms a part.

CARL NORDENFALK

Abbreviations

Munich, 1931   *Mittelalterliche Miniaturen* (Munich: J. Rosenthal, Briennerstrasse 47, 193

Baltimore, 1949   *Illuminated Books of the Middle Ages and Renaissance* (Baltimore: The Baltimore Museum of Art, 1949)

National Gallery, 1950   *Rosenwald Collection: An Exhibition of Recent Acquisitions* (Washington D.C.: National Gallery of Art, 1950)

Los Angeles, 1953–1954   *Mediaeval and Renaissance Illuminated Manuscripts* (Los Angeles: Los Angeles County Museum, 1953–1954)

Hartford, 1965   *An Exhibition of Italian Panels and Manuscripts from the Thirteenth and Fourteenth Centuries in Honor of Richard Offner* (Hartford: Wadsworth Atheneum, 1965)

Trenton, 1971   *A Selection of X–XV Century Medieval Miniatures from the National Gallery of Art, Rosenwald Collection* (Trenton: New Jersey State Museu 1971)

South Bend, 1972   *Mediaeval Manuscripts from the Lessing J. Rosenwald Collection* (South Bend: Art Gallery, University of Notre Dame, 1972)

Lugt   Frits Lugt, *Les Marques de collections de dessins et d'estampes* (Amsterda 1921; supplement: The Hague, 1956)

Note to the Catalogue

*All measurements are given in millimeters
and parenthetically in inches.
Wherever space permits, pieces in the Gallery's
collection are reproduced full size.
Whenever this is not possible, in most cases a
full-size detail is shown.*

*All the pieces are of vellum and are written
in Latin unless otherwise indicated.
Miniature condition is graded: Fair, Good, Very Good,
and Excellent.*

*Photographs of objects in the Gallery's
collection were made by the photographic
staff of the National Gallery of Art,
Henry B. Beville, Chief.
Photographs of supplementary materials were
kindly provided by the institutions owning those pieces.*

The Catalogue

I

Leaf from a Giant Bible

Four scenes from the First Book of Samuel
Central Italy (Rome?), late 11th century
B-17,714
414 x 273   (16 3/8 x 10 3/4)

Caroline minuscule script; 2 columns of 56 lines (at least 414 x c. 115 x c. 255 mm)

CONDITION   (F/G) Vellum extensively rubbed and wrinkled; horizontal crease at mid-point; extensively tattered and notched, especially along right side; pigments faded and rubbed; trimmed all around

PROVENANCE   Pattern of wear indicates that it once served as a cover guard for a manuscript; A. Mettler, Saint Gall (up to 1929); Delaunay, The Hague; Baron von Thyssen, Rohoncz Castle (by 1930); E. Rosenthal, Berkeley; L. J. Rosenwald, Jenkintown (1950); National Gallery of Art (1950)

EXHIBITED   *Sammlung Schloss Rohoncz* (Munich: Neue Pinakothek, 1930), no. 83, illus.; National Gallery, 1950, no. 1, illus.; Los Angeles, 1953–1954, no. 8; Trenton, 1971, no. 1

BIBLIOGRAPHY   Mm.-Mensing et Fils (Frederik Muller et Cie), *Catalogue d'une collection de manuscrits à miniatures des IXe-XVe siècles: Collection d'un amateur Suisse* [Sale Catalogue, Nov. 22, 1929] (Amsterdam 1929), lot 49, illus.; *Otto Kurz,* "Ein insulares Muster-buchblatt und die byzantinische Psalterillustration," *Byzantinisch-Neugriechische Jahrbücher 14* (1937–1938), 89n.; Hugo Buchthal, *The Miniatures of the Paris Psalter* (London 1938), p. 49; Edward B. Garrison, "Twelfth-Century Initial Styles of Central Italy: Indices for the Dating of Manuscripts, Part I. Synthesis (Concluded)," *Studies in the History of Mediaeval Italian Painting 1, no. 2* (Autumn 1953), 56f.; Edward B. Garrison, "Contributions to the History of Twelfth-Century Umbro-Roman Painting, Part II. Materials (Continued): v, The Italian-Byzantine-Romanesque Fusion in the First Quarter of the Twelfth Century," *Studies in the History of Mediaeval Italian Painting 3, no. 1* (Spring 1957), 90ff., 98ff., fig. 116; Knut Berg, *Studies in Tuscan Twelfth-Century Illumination* (Oslo 1968), p. 87n

Fig. 1c. Verso detail, 1:1

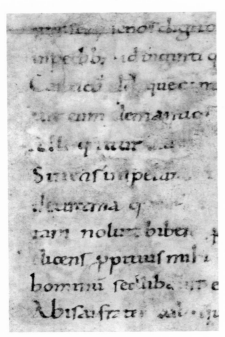

Fig. 1b. Recto detail, 1:1

RECTO *(fig. 1b)* Chapter list (series B) beginning in chapter 64 (*holocausta . . .*) through the end (chapter 98, numbered 95).[1]

VERSO *(figs. 1a, 1c)* Title to Samuel 1: *Incip[it] Samuhel Lib[er] Regu[m] Primus.* Top row (1 Sam. 1:9–18): Hannah (*Anna*) and Elkanah (*Helchana*) before the Priest Eli (*Heli*) praying for a son. Middle row (1 Sam. 1:24–2:10): Hannah (and Elkanah) present the infant Samuel (inscription nearly illegible) to Eli. (The two non-inscribed men behind Eli are probably his evil sons, Hophni and Phinehas). Bottom row (1 Sam. 16:13; 1 Sam. 17:49): Samuel (*Samuel P[ro]ph[e]ta*) anoints David (*D[avi]d*), and David slays Goliath (*Goliath*).

Hannah, Eli, and David wear light yellow undergarments with folds delineated in red and white. The capes of Elkanah, Eli, and David, as well as Samuel's mantle, are bright red. The tunics worn by Elkanah and Samuel, and Goliath's armor are grayish blue; the border alternates red, dark green, and blue.

This rubbed and tattered leaf, which originally faced the beginning of Samuel 1 (Now there was a certain man of Ramathaim-zophim, of Mount Ephraim, and his name was Elkanah . . .), is the only remaining fragment of an illustrated Giant Bible of the type produced in the region of Rome during the later eleventh and early twelfth centuries.[2] The program of illustration of its parent manuscript probably exceeded that typical of this series of Bibles which characteristically included a full-page narrative illustration for Genesis, and only simple, full-figure author portraits for the various books. Moreover, these scenes of Hannah and Elkanah are extremely rare in medieval art, with only a few isolated examples pre-dating this fragment.

More than twenty years ago Edward Garrison noted stylistic similarities between the Rosenwald leaf and a number of the incipit miniatures in a Giant Bible in Parma (Biblioteca Palatina, cod. lat. 386).[3] He suggested that the Rosenwald leaf, the Parma Bible, and a Giant Bible in Genoa (Biblioteca Comunale, cod. R.B. 2554.2) comprised a sub-group within the series of Umbro-Roman Giant Bibles, associated in the following manner: the illuminator of the Genoa Bible ("Genoa Master"), decorated part of the Parma Bible, the majority of which was done by his follower ("pupil of the Genoa Bible Master"); the Rosenwald miniaturist is stylistically related to the "pupil." He dated the group to the late first quarter of the twelfth century on the basis of script and ornament style, and suggested a localization in Umbria (instead of Rome), citing three lines of evidence: 1) thirteenth-century notes in the Parma Bible refer to an Umbrian church; 2) the rough figure style of the group suggests a provincial origin; and 3) the Genesis illustration in the Parma Bible is closely related to its counterpart in a Giant Bible known to have been in Perugia from the late twelfth century (Perugia, Biblioteca Comunale, cod. L.59).[4]

Although not considering the Rosenwald leaf directly nor re-examining its sub-group in specific, Knut Berg, nonetheless, emphasized the specifically Roman artistic and political milieu from which he felt the early Giant Bibles arose. He suggests that the Giant Bible "edition" and its characteristic geometrical initial ornament are the products of an eleventh-century Papal reform movement which culminated in the Pontificate of Gregory VII (1073–1085).[5] A Papal association would account for their great popularity and wide distribu-

tion, and an origin in Rome, whose instability did not allow for the development of a refined artistic tradition, would account for the rustic figure style of the early Giant Bibles. In agreement with Berg's chronology, we would prefer an earlier date for the Rosenwald fragment than Garrison's, or well before 1100.

The dependency of the Italian geometric initial on Carolingian (especially Touronian) models has been noted by a number of scholars.[6] Within this context it is of special interest that the Rosenwald leaf duplicates the iconographic program of the Touronian Bibles in prefacing a biblical book with superimposed rows of narrative scenes based on the subsequent text.[7] Further, one of the few extant manuscripts with illustrations of events surrounding the birth of Samuel is the Carolingian Bible of Charles the Bald preserved since the ninth century in the Church of San Paolo fuori le Mura in Rome.[8] Architectual motifs, costumes, and poses in the Rosenwald miniature are reminiscent of their counterparts in the San Paolo Bible, with the figures of David and Goliath showing especially close parallels.

1. *Biblia Sacra: Iuxta latinam vulgatam versionem ad codicum fidem: Liber Samuhelis* (Rome 1944), pp. 26ff.
2. For a list of Bibles of this type see Berg, 1968, 87n.; and Knut Berg, "Notes on the Dates of Some Early Giant Bibles," *Acta Institutum Romanum Norvegiae 2* (1965), 167ff.
3. Garrison, 1953, p. 56. Four years later Garrison elaborated on that study (Garrison, 1957, pp. 90ff., pp. 98ff., fig. 116). For illustrations of the relevant miniatures in the Parma Bible, see Garrison, 1957, figs. 107–115 (esp. 113).
4. Garrison, 1957, pp. 90f.
5. Berg, 1968, pp. 18f.
6. Berg, 1968, p. 18.
7. See Wilhelm Koehler, *Die Karolingischen Miniaturen: Die Schule von Tours: I, 2: Die Bilder* (Berlin 1933), pp. 109ff.
8. Photograph in the Princeton Index of Christian Art.

2

Two Bifolios from a Giant Bible

Mark (A) *Luke* (B)
Tuscany, last quarter 12th
century
B-22,920 (A), B-22,919 (B)
540 x 365 (21 1/4 x 14 3/8)

Late Caroline minuscule script; 2 columns of 54 lines
(437 x 110 x 263 mm)

CONDITION (G/VG) Colors and detail generally fresh with only minor rubbing; vellum has seriously deteriorated (by mold) at gutter and fore-edge; two sets of late eighteenth-century notes in French:
A, 2v (fore-edge) *no. 24 8(ter);* (bottom) *sept cahiers délibérations depuis le 29 Juillet 1790 jusques au 28 mai 1792; no. 24. no. 8 (ter).;*
B, 2v (fore-edge): *14;* (gutter): *no. 27;* (intercolumnar) *4 cahiers des Lanctieres (?) de beaux à farine depuis le 8 aôut 1790 jusques au 17 vendemain (?) au 4. no. 27 . R°-14(ter).*

PROVENANCE Notations on two bifolios suggest they were used as loose covers for accounts and other documents during the occupation of the Rhineland by the French Revolutionary Armies; E. Rosenthal, Berkeley; L. J. Rosenwald, Jenkintown (1963); National Gallery of Art (1964)

EXHIBITED Trenton, 1971, nos. 2, 5, illus.

A, 1 RECTO Matt. 27:31 ([*indu*]*er*[*un*]*t eu*[*m*] . . .)—Matt. 28:20; the first three lines of the Mark prologue.

A, 1 VERSO *(figs. 2a, 2c)* Completion of the Mark prologue; Mark *capitula* (24); Mark 1:1—Mark 1:10 (. . . *et ma*[*nentem*]); and on Mark's lectern: (Mark 1:1) *Initium ev*[*an*]*g*[*e*]*lii ihu* . . . .

Fig. 2c. Verso detail, A, 1:1

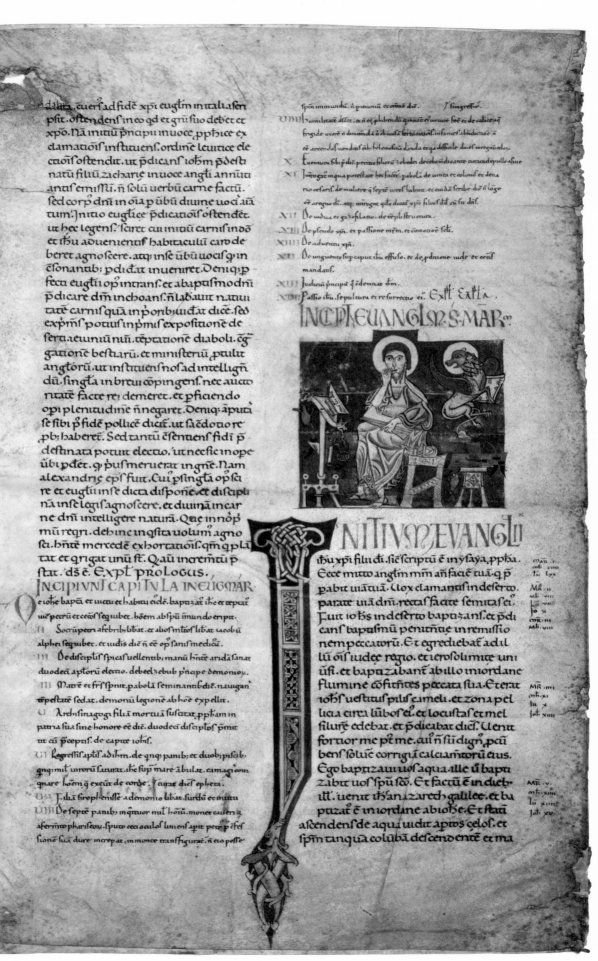

[Left column]

...dita, euersad fide xpi euglm in italia scri
psit. ostendens in eo qd et grm suo debet et
xpo. Na initiu pnapu inuoce. pphice ex
clamatois instituens. ordine leuitice ele
ctiois ostendit. ut pdicans iohm pdest
natu filiu zacharie in uoce angli annuti
antis emissu. n solu uerbu carne factu.
sed corp dm in oia p ubu diuine uocis iniu
tum. Initio euglice pdicatiois ostendet.
ut hec legens saret cui initiu carnis indo
et ihu aduenientis habitaculu caro de
beret agnoscere. atqz inse ubu uocis qi in
consonantib: pdicat inueniret. Deniqz p
fecti euglii opis intrans. et a baptismo dni
pdicare dm inchoans. nlaba uit natiui
tate carnis qua in prioribus dicere. sed
ex pms potius in pms expositione de
serta. ieiuniu nm. teptatione diaboli. co
gatione bestiaru. et ministeriu ptulit
angtoru. ut instituens nos ad intelligen
du. singla in breui copingens. nec aucto
ritate facte rei demeret. et pfaciendo
opis plenitudine n negaret. Deniqz a piuta
se sibi p fide pollice dicit. ut sacdotio re
pb: haberet. Sed tantu csentiens fidi p
destinata potuit electio. ut nec sic in ope
ubi pdet. qi pus meruerat in gne. Nam
alexandrie eps fuit. Cui psingta op sci
re. et euglii in se dicta dispone. et discipli
na in se legis agnoscere. et diuina incar
ne dm intelligere natura. Que in no p
mu regni. dehinc ingsta uolum agno
sci. hute mercede exhortatiois. qm q plu
rat et qrigat unu ff. Qau incremtu p
stat. ds e. Expt PROLOGUS.
INCIPIVNT CAPITVLA IN EUG MAR
I De iohe bapa et uictu et habitu eide. bapatz ihc et tepat
uic petru et ceos sequibet. hoem ab spu imundo eripit.
II Socru petri a febrib: libat. et alios m teos libat. iacob et
alphei sequibet. et uidis die n ee op saius medici.
III De discipulis spicas uellentib: manu hnte arida sanat
duodeci aptoru electio. debeelzebub p nape demoniou.
IIII Mare et fri spmt. pabola seminantib: die. nauigan
tepestate sedat. demonu legione ab hoe expellit.
V Archisinagogi filia mortua suscitat. pphiam in
patria sua sine honore ee die. duodeci disciplos pmit
ut cu pcepris. de capite iohis.
VI Regressis aptis ad ihm. de qnqz panib: et duobus piscib:
qnqz milia uiroru saturat. ihc sup mare abulat. et magis ori
qnare hoem qi exeut de corde. / a quare dies epheta.
VII Filia sirophenisse a demonio libat. surdu et mutu
VIII De septe panib: in quatuor mil hoiu. moner euen a
a fermto phariseou. sputu ceci oculis lumen apit petri cfes
sione sua dure increpat. in monte transfigurat. n eta posse

spm immundu. a pleunmu ee oiono da. / si ingressur.
VIIII am libratie decor. ee in eo ph bendu qi nno o eos uie soe ee de alicoaq
frigide uocet n dimdia a n beatu sorti actis ei. in sa nec s abdicinoe n
ee arecedos uecidens ab hoi ones uis danda erqa difficile dues mregulos
X Euentura sibi p die. petini siloru u ebedei decem oo mi ci aare cu ni ede pullo asine
XI Inuoqz qua potestate hec facit. pabola de uineis et colonis ee dena
rio cesaris. de muliere qi septe uiros habuit. ee cuda scribe die n loge
ee a regno di. atqz mirqat qdo dicat xps filius dd cu sit dns.
XII De uidua et qi sofilauit. de templi structura.
XIII De pseudo xpis. et passione mm. et connectioe sci.
XIIII De aduentu xpi.
XV De unguento sup caput ihu effuso. ee de pditione iude. ee oeus
mandaus.
XVI Iudicu pncipu qi edemnat ihm.
XVII Passio ihu. sepultura et resurrectio ei. EXPL CAPLA.

INCIP PL EUANGLM S MAR

INITIVM EUANGLII
ihu xpi filu di. sic scriptu e in ysaya. ppha.
Ecce mitto anglm mm an facie tua. qi p
pabit uia tua. Uox clamantis in deserto.
parate uia dni. rectas fa cite semitas ei.
Fuit iohs in deserto baptisans. et pdi
cans baptismu penitntie in remissio
nem peccatoru. Et egrediebat ad il
lu ois iudee regio. et ierosolimite uni
usi. et baptizabant ab illo in iordane
flumine cofintes peccata sua. Et erat
iohs uestitus pilis cameli. et zona pel
licia circa lubos ei. et locustas et mel
siluestre edebat. et pdicabat dicens. Uenit
fortior me pt me. cui n su dign. pcu
bens soluere corrigia calciamntoru eius.
Ego baptizaui uos aqua ille u bapti
zabit uos spu sco. Et factu e in die
bus ill. uenit ihc a nazareth galilee. et ba
ptizat e in iordane abiohe. Et statim
ascendens de aqua uidit apos celos. et
spm tanqua columba descendente et ma

[Right margin notes]
matt
mfit cm
ta lxx

MR n
mfi xi
Lu x
oms xn
Mat. xvii

MR m
mfit xi
Lu x
Ioh xvi

MR v
mfit xvii
Lu xvii
Ioh xv

Mark, dressed in a pink mantle over a blue tunic, is set before a background of blue, burgundy, and dark green. All furniture is bright yellow, as are haloes and initial fillets. The shaft ornament of the initial is blue and red; its background dark blue, red, and burgundy.

In spite of its rough figure style the portrait of Mark closely corresponds to one of the eight Evangelist portrait types known in Byzantine art from the early Middle Ages: profile view with one hand raised to the chin, the other holding a large vellum leaf across the lap, and the feet slightly separated.[1]

A, 2 RECTO   Mark 12:14 (*an n[on] dabim[us]* ...)—Mark 13:24.

A, 2 VERSO   Mark 13:24—14:48 (*Et re[spondens]*).

B, 1 RECTO   Luke *capitula* from IV (*et fortiore[m]* ...)—XXVIII.

B, 1 VERSO (*figs. 2b, 2d*)   Completion of *capitula* (XXVIII); Luke 1:1—Luke 1:47 (*... salutari meo*); and on Luke's lectern: (Luke 1:5) *Herodi regi iudee sac[er]dos* ....

Luke is dressed in a green mantle over a blue tunic; his furniture is white, outlined in red. The initial fillets are pale yellow; the shaft ornament blue, red, green, and burgundy against a background of bright blue and burgundy.

B, 2 RECTO   Luke 16:24 (*digiti sui* ...)—Luke 18:22.

B, 2 VERSO   Luke 18:22—Luke 19:48 (*erat audien[s]*).

These two bifolios, removed from the binding of an unknown Giant Bible,[2] are ornamented with geometric incipit initials (for the Gospels of Mark and Luke) of a type characteristic of Central Italian illumination of the twelfth century.[3] More specifically, their orderly repertoire of highly stylized and compartmentalized ornamental motifs, and their limited range of saturated colors (including yellow fillets) associate them with the late geometric style, identified by Knut Berg as appearing for the first time fully developed in the Corbolinus Bible of 1140 (Florence, Biblioteca Laurenziana, cod. conv. soppr. 680),[4] and flourishing in Tuscany, with only minor changes, during the second half of the twelfth century. More highly refined, yet less stylized parallels for the Rosenwald I and Q may be found (respectively) in the Montalcino Bible (second illuminator) (Montalcino, Museo Comunale, cod. Bible, vol. II),[5] and in a Sacramentary in the Pierpont Morgan Library (cod. M737),[6] both assigned by Berg to Tuscan illuminators of the second half of the century.

While full correspondence in page and text-block dimensions, as well as ruling pattern, lines per page, and provenance, confirm a common origin for these two bifolios in the same codex, a number of significant differences distinguish their figure and ornament styles, and thus suggest the participation of two illuminators.[7] The Luke miniature is generally more geometric, with a carefully defined border and a precisely drawn fillet interlace. Its drapery style is completely linear and its furniture is rendered in white (bare vellum). On the other hand, the Mark miniature (with initial), shows much stronger colors;[8] a less precise fillet interlace; a dependence on rosette and half-leaf shaft ornament (instead of an interlace as in Q); different formulae for the articulation of the mouth and beard; a modeled drapery style (based on the so-called nested-v fold);[9] deep yellow accessories; and a rather free use of expressive animal heads. Finally, Mark is shown with his accompanying symbol, the lion, while Luke's counterpart, the calf, is absent.

aquo unus ex latronibz erodem? ad pa disu duce. ab hora sexta usq; ad nona dies
obscurat? e. et ihsm emittente uelu tepl sciss? e. qd uisu centurio et q ade
rant dnm magnifica?t. ioseph postulat corp et sepelit. q muliere? relinq
Nutiant mulieres uisiones angloru nec credut disc. Eos inuenunt.
Eunt ex duo in castella. in panis fractioe xpm cognosc. et reusi disc in
dicunt qb; apparuit. et plagas no credent; ostend. accp scec et fauu
edondu accep. alloqt aplos. et cor eoru aperit ad intelligdu. qb; copan
Et ut illic eent donec in eos uenerit uirtus ammonet. oportuerit.
et bndixit eos et recessit reliquq; laudantes dnm in tepl. EXPT

QUONIAM QUIDE
multi conati sunt ordinare narratione que in nob co
plete sunt reru. sicut tradider nob q ab initio ipsi ui
derut. et ministri fuer sermonis. uisu e et m asse
cuto a principio. oia dilignt exordine tibi scribere
optime theophile. ut cognosca eoru uiboru de
qb; erudit es ueritate. Fuit in diebz herodis
regis iudee sacdos qda noe zacharias de uice a
bia. et uxor illi de filiabz aaron. et nom ei heli
sabeth. Erant au iusti ambo an dnm inceden
tes in oibz mandatis et iustificatioibz dni sine
querela. Et no erat illis filius. eo qd eet helisabeth
sterilis. et ambo pcessissent in diebz suis. Factu
e au cu sacdotio fungeret zacharias in ordine
uicis sue an dnm scdm csuetudine sacdotii. sor
te exiit ut incensu poneret. ingress in templu
dni. Et ois multitudo erat ppli orans foris hora
incensi. Apparuit au illi angls dni stans a dex
tris altaris incensi. Et zacharias turbat e uiden.
et timor irruit sup eu. Ait au ad illu angls. Ne
timeas zacharia. qm exaudita e deprecatio tua.
uxor tua helisabeth pariet t filiu. et uocab

nom ei iohm. Et erit gaudiu t et exultatio. et multi
in natiuitate ei gaudebt. Erit eni magn cora dno.
et uinu et sicera no bibet. Et spu sco replebit ad huc.
ex utero matris sue. Et multos filioru isrl cuertet ad
dnm dm ipsoru. Et ipse pcedet an illu in spu et
uirtute helie. ut cuertat corda patru in filios. et
incredibiles ad prudentia iustoru. parare dno ple
be pfecta. Et dixit zacharias ad anglm. Un hoc
scia? ego eni su senex. et uxor mea pcessit in diebz
suis. Et respondens angls dixit. Ego su gabriel q
asto an dm. et missus su loq ad te. et hec t euagli
zare. Et ecce eris tacens et no potis loq usq; in die
q hec fiant. pro eo qd no credidisti uerb meis. q imple
buntur in tpr suo. Et erat plebs expectans zacha
ria. et mirabant q tardaret ipse in teplo. Egress
au no potat loq ad illos. Et cognouer q uisione
uidiss; in teplo. Et ipse erat innuens illis. et pman
sit mut. Et factu e ut impleta s dies officii ei. abiit
in domu sua. Post hos au dies ccepit helisabeth
uxor ei. et occultabat se msibz qnq; dies. Qa sic
fecit dns in diebz qb; respex auferre obpbriu
int hoes. In mse au sexto. missus e gabrihel
angls a do in ciuitate galilee. cui nomen nazareth
ad uirgine desponsata uiro cui nom ioseph de
domo dd. et nom uirginis maria. Et ingressu
angls ad ea dix. Aue gra plena. dns tecu. bndicta
tu in mulierib;. Que cu audiss; turbata e in ser
mone ei. et cogitabat qlis eet ista salutatio. Et ait an
gls ei. Ne timeas maria. inuenisti eni gram apd dnm.
Ecce cacipies in utero. et paries filiu. et uocabis nom ei
ihm. Hic erit magn. et filius altissimi uocabit. Et
dabit illi dns ds sede dd patris ei. et regnabit in
domo iacob in etnu. et regni ei no erit finis. Dixit au
maria ad anglm. Qo fiet istud. qm uiru no co
gnosco? Et respondens angls dixit. Sps scs super
ueniet in te. et uirt altissimi obubrabit t. Ideoq;
et q nascet ex te scm. uocabit filius di. Et ecce
helisabeth cognata tua. et ipsa ccepit filiu in se
nectute sua. Et hic msis e sext illi q uocat sterilis.
qa no erit impossibile apud dm oe ubu. Dix
au maria. Ecce ancilla dni. fiat m scdm ubu tuu.
Et discesit ab illa angls. Exurges au maria in diebz ill; abiit
m montana cu festinatioe in ciuitate iuda. et in
trauit in domu zacharie. et salutauit helisa
beth. Et factu e ut audiit salutatione marie
helisabeth. exultauit infans in utero ei. Et repleta
e spu sco helisabeth. et exclamauit uoce ma
gna et dix. Bndicta tu int mulieres. et bndict
fruc uentris tui. Et un hoc m. ut ueniat mat
dni mei ad me. Ecce eni ut facta e uox saluta
tionis tue in auribz meis. exultauit in gaudio ifans
in utero meo. Et beata q credidisti. qm pficient ea q
dicta s tibi a dno. Et ait maria. Magnificat au
mea dnm. et exultauit sps ms in do salutari meo.

The rustic figure style of the Rosenwald Evangelists[10] as well as the reduced, highly abstract treatment of the vegetal motifs within the shaft of the I, suggest an advanced stage in the development of the late geometric style, and an origin away from the leading workshops of the Florentine and Pisan school. Specifically, both ornament and figure style show similarities to an initial portrait of Job on a single leaf fragment formerly in the Hoepli Collection,[11] localized by Berg to Siena, and assigned to the late twelfth century.[12]

1. See Robert Bergman, "Portraits of the Evangelists in Greek Manuscripts," *Illuminated Greek Manuscripts from American Collections*, ed. Gary Vikan (Princeton: Princeton Art Museum, 1973), pp. 44ff., fig. 12.
2. Judging from the ratio of text to page, bifolio A probably would have comprised leaves 2 and 7 of a quaternion, and bifolio B would have comprised leaves 1 and 8 of a quaternion.
3. Knut Berg, *Studies in Tuscan Twelfth-Century Illumination* (Oslo 1968), pp. 11ff.; and Edward B. Garrison, "Twelfth-Century Initial Styles of Central Italy," a series of articles in: *Studies in the History of Mediaeval Italian Painting 1–4* (1953–1962), passim.
4. Berg, 1968, pp. 50ff.; no. 58, figs. 112–118.
5. Berg, 1968, no. 110, esp. figs. 420–422. Compare especially the fillet interlace, and the shaft ornament and compartmentalization.
6. Berg, 1968, no. 111, fig. 207. The "VD" monogram shows, in more sophisticated form, fillet interlaces, shaft compartmentalization, interlace ornament, and corner rosettes of the type found in the Rosenwald initial Q.
7. The script also shows differences. That of bifolio A is more ornate and larger (c. 26 letters per 100 mm of standard line) than that of bifolio B (c. 35 letters per 100 mm).
8. This difference is in part accounted for by the fact that the Mark miniature is painted on the grain or "hair" side of the vellum which characteristically holds pigment better than does the "flesh" side, upon which the Luke miniature is painted.
9. The nested-v, ultimately Byzantine in origin, spread throughout Central Italy during the second quarter of the twelfth century. It is to be seen in its most extreme form in the Pantheon Bible (Rome, Vatican Library, cod. lat. 12958). See Garrison, 1961, IV, no. 2, pp. 118ff., esp. figs. 87–88.
10. A more elegant treatment of the Luke portrait with striking parallels of pose and composition, is found in the Avila Bible (Madrid, Bibl. Nacional, cod. vitr. 15, fol. 343r). See Garrison, 1960, IV, no. 1, fig. 8 (attribution to the early third quarter of the twelfth century).
11. Pietro Toesca, *La Collezione di Ulrico Hoepli* (Milan 1930), no. 1, fig. 6, pl. 1.
12. Berg, 1968, p. 197. The attribution is based on similarities to manuscripts in Sienese libraries showing a debased initial style and rough illustrations.

Fig. 2d. Verso detail, B, 1 : 1

3

Leaf from a Choir Book (Gradual)

Nativity with Six Dominican Monks

Italy, c. 1275

B-13,522

468 x 360   (18 1/2 x 14 1/4)

Fig. 3c. Verso, detail, 1:1

Gothic minuscule script with four-line staff in red (33 mm); 6 lines, 5 accompanied by staffs (top staff trimmed) (356 x 236 mm)

CONDITION   (VG) Colors and facial detail very fresh; vellum wrinkled and pigment flaked toward bottom; trimmed along top (one staff lost); two lines, one staff erased above miniature; 30 mm tear along right edge

PROVENANCE   Said to have been bought by a British collector from a convent near Bologna in the late nineteenth century; A. Sambon, Paris; Zinser; L. J. Rosenwald, Jenkintown (1946); National Gallery of Art (1946)

EXHIBITED   Baltimore, 1949, no. 37, illus.; *Medieval and Renaissance Music Manuscripts* (Toledo: The Toledo Museum of Art, 1953), no. 37, illus.; Los Angeles, 1953–1954, illus.; *Pages from Medieval and Renaissance Illuminated Manuscripts from the Xth to the Early XVIth Centuries* (Berkeley: University Art Gallery, 1963), no. 9 illus.; Hartford, 1965, no. 89, illus.

RECTO *(fig. 3b)*   Offertory for the daybreak Christmas mass, beginning: *commovebitur: parata . . .* ; followed by the Communion response.

VERSO *(figs. 3a, 3c; Colorplate 1)*   Completion of the Communion response from the recto, followed by rubrics (all erased) and four staffs (covered by miniature). The miniature, originally not foreseen by the scribe, thus would have preceded the Introit for the third Christmas mass (that during the day), beginning: *Puer Natus est.* (Isaiah 9:6: A Child is born to us, and a son is given to us. . . .)

The Virgin attends the swaddled Christ Child in the center of the Nativity grotto. An unusually small Joseph is seated at the right, while two attendants bathe the Christ Child to the left. Eight angels proclaim the birth above on two banderoles: (left) *Gloria in excelsis Deo* and (right) *Et in terra pax ho [min]ib[us] bone vo[lentatis].* (Luke 2:14, the first Antiphon *in evangelio* at Lauds for Christmas Day.) From beneath three sets of compound arches, six Dominican Monks look up in adoration, holding two banderoles: (left) *Ora pro nobis quia mulier sanctaes,* and (right) *Ora pro nobis s[a]c[r]a Dei Genetrix.*[1]

This miniature originally faced the beginning of the third Christmas Day mass in a large Dominican Gradual (the choir book for the mass, including antiphons for the Introit, Offertory, and Communion, as well as a Gradual, Tract, and Alleluia). Stylistically, it falls within that period of Italian illumination of the later thirteenth and early fourteenth centuries which is characterized by a confluence of Byzantine and Gothic elements. Among the several centers through which these influences were absorbed (including Sicily and the area of Naples,[2] the Veneto,[3] Emilia—with its apparent center at Bologna,[4] Pisa, and Florence)[5] there existed a stylistic similitude, which has made it difficult for scholars to isolate local schools.[6]

Among the miniatures showing greatest similarity to the Rosenwald Nativity are those in two large codices tentatively, but by no means certainly, attributed to Bologna: a copy of Petrus Lombardus, *Liber IV. sententiarum,* in Vienna (Nationalbibliothek, cod. 1415),[7] and a Dominican Bible, recently in the possession of H.P. Kraus, New York.[8] Both show a comparable ornamental background arabesque;[9] lurching poses; hard, linear highlights; and a highly stylized articulation of the faces (which leaves the form of the mouth unclear). The Kraus

Bible even shows a profusion of singing birds very similar to those of our miniature.[10]

More generally, several elements of the Rosenwald leaf bear comparison with the much more highly Byzantinizing and monumental miniatures in the *Epistolary of Giovanni da Gaibana* (Perugia, Biblioteca Universitaria, cod. s.s.), produced in the Veneto in 1259.[11] Most similar are the facial types, and the stylization of the hair (like that of Joseph, which descends in coarse strands from the top center of the head). Finally, with the Conradin Bible in Baltimore (Walters Art Gallery, cod. w152), which is probably a product of southern Italy (see note 6), it shares its expressive poses, Byzantinizing faces, and highly articulated drapery.[12]

1. Notice the liberties that the illuminator has taken with the relative sizes of his figures (the Virgin and Joseph) and with the posture of the two center monks, who are forced to adapt to the compositional requirements of the banderoles. While both features are characteristically medieval; the singing birds add an element of incipient realism.

2. Angela Daneu Lattanzi, *Lineamenti di storia della miniatura in Sicilia* (Florence 1966), pp. 49ff.; and Angela Daneu Lattanzi, *Una Bibbia prossima alla 'Bibbia di Manfredi'* (Palermo 1955), passim.

3. Claudio Bellinati and Sergio Bettini, *L'Epistolario miniato di Giovanni da Gaibana* (Vicenza 1968), pp. 81ff.; and Edward Garrison, "A Giant Venetian Bible of the Earlier Thirteenth Century," *Scritti di storia dell'arte in onore di Mario Salmi* (Rome 1961), vol. 1, esp. p. 365.

4. Adalberto Conte Erbach di Fuerstenau, "La Miniatura Bolognese nel trecento (studi su Nicolò di Giacomo)," *L'Arte 14* (1911), 1ff.; Giorgio Castelfranco, "Contributi alla storia dela miniatura Bolognese del '200," *Bologna* (1937), pp. 7ff.

5. Mario Salmi, "Un Evangeliario miniato Fiorentino," *Rivista d'arte 19* (1937), 1ff.; and Paolo D'Ancona, "Un Miniatore Fiorentino della scuola di Cimabue," *Rivista d'arte 16* (1934), 105ff.

6. Dorothy Miner, in her analysis of the Conradin Bible (Baltimore, Walters Art Galley, cod. w152), remained undecided as to whether its combination of late western Romanesque and early Gothic, and Byzantine elements reflected an origin in southern Italy (region of Naples), or in Bologna. See Dorothy Miner, "The Conradin Bible: A Masterpiece of Italian Illumination," *Apollo 84, no. 58* (Dec. 1966), 471ff.

7. Hermann J. Hermann, *Die Italienischen Handschriften des Dugento und Trecento, 1. Bis zur Mitte des XIV. Jahrhunderts (Beschreibendes Verzeichnis der illuminierten Handschriften in Österreich, V, 1)* (Leipzig 1928), no. 66, pls. xxxvi–xxxviii, 1.

8. H. P. Kraus, *Fifty Medieval and Renaissance Manuscripts*, [Sale Catalogue no. 88, n.d.] (New York, n.d.), no. 33. pls. pages 74, 148–149. The Rosenwald miniature is closest to the style of the (secondary) illuminator who executed the first miniature to the Bible prologue (illus. p. 148, upper left).

9. It should be noted that the type of arabesque is especially characteristic of fourteenth-century Perugian miniatures (see cat. 9). According to a recent catalogue (Hartford, 1965, no. 89) Dr. Mirella Levi D'Ancona suggested a localization for the Rosewald leaf in Perugia, ". . . but under strong Sienese influence."

10. Kraus, n.d., illus. p. 149.

11. Bellinati and Bettini, 1968, passim. (facsimile).

12. Lattanzi, 1966, figs. 51–54; Miner, 1966, passim.

Fig. 3b. Recto

4

Initial F from a Choir Book (Antiphonary?)

Birth and Naming of John the Baptist
Abruzzi (?); Bologna (?),
Late 13th century
B-15,886
221 x 158   (8 3/4 x 6 3/16)

Fig. 4b. Verso

Gothic minuscule script with four-line staff in red (30 mm)

CONDITION   (VG) Facial detail and most colors well preserved, except for blue background which is rubbed in several areas; irregularly trimmed along left side

PROVENANCE   E. Rosenthal, Berkeley; L. J. Rosenwald, Jenkintown (1949); National Gallery of Art (1950)

SISTER MINIATURE   Tübingen, R. A. Bohnke Collection: single initial C (120 x 145 mm); Saint Nicholas Giving Money to the Poor Nobleman (*fig. 4c*)[1]

RECTO *(fig. 4a)* (?) Beginning of a Response in First Nocturns for the Feast of John the Baptist (June 24): F[*uit homo missus*]. (John 1:6-7: There was a man sent from God. . . .)[2]

Elizabeth, in a pale burgundy mantel over an orange tunic, reclines on two pillows at the left, while Zacharias,[3] in orange over dark blue, is seated at the right. Elizabeth looks away from John, perhaps as an expression of the pains of childbirth, which are apparently mirrored in the stylized lines of her face. The child, who is suspended in a cradle, is attended by a figure in orange; a second attendant adjusts the pillow of Elizabeth.

Below, the "neighbors and cousins" described in the biblical account (Luke 1:58), congregate before Zacharias, waiting as he inscribes his child's name on a tablet: *Ioh*[*annes*] *es*[*t*] *n*[*omen eius*]. The garments of the group are bright orange and dark blue; Zacharias wears a pale burgundy mantle over an orange tunic. The curtain backgrounds above and below are formed of patterns of brown, pale burgundy, and orange. The initial, comprising the same colors, is set against a deep blue background.

VERSO *(fig. 4b)* The end of the Response from the recto: [*p*]*lebem per*[*fectam*]; followed by a verse(?) (a variant of that which customarily includes the phrase: ". . . *in deserto predicans* . . .[?]).[4]

This initial originally marked the celebration of the Feast Day of John the Baptist (June 24) in a large Italian choir book, another fragment of which is now in a private European collection.[5] While the story of the birth and naming of John is related only in Luke (1:57–63), these scenes head a sung passage drawn from the Gospel of John (1:6-7: There was a man sent from God . . .). Thus, a haloed eagle, symbol of John the Evangelist, is enclosed by the initial at the upper left.

Stylistically this miniature, like that which precedes it in this catalogue (cat. 3), falls within that period of Italian illumination (late duecento, early trecento) characterized by the absorption of Byzantine and trans-alpine influences. In this case Gothic elements predominate, with Byzantine formulae only faintly recalled in the stylization of the face, and in drapery patterns. Professor Carlo Bertelli has suggested that our fragment was painted by a master from the Abruzzi.[6] On the other hand, it shows similarities to miniatures traditionally ascribed to Bologna, circa 1300. The decoration in a series of choir books from San Domenico at Gubbio (now in the communal archives of that city),[7] shows a comparable taste for ornament (especially large Xs); haloes ringed by sets of three dots; thick, leafy initial stalks; and similar figure types and drapery modeling. Also worthy of comparison are several legal and medical codices in the Bodleian Library, Oxford (cods. conon. pat. lat. 144; e mus. 19; conon. misc. 416; conon. misc. 494),[8] and the Nationalbibliothek, Vienna (cods. 2252, 2286, series nova 4444),[9] all ascribed to Bologna not long before or after 1300.

Finally, a parallel facial type is found in the *Statuti dei Falegnami*, a Bolognese manuscript dated 1270.[10]

1. Karl and Faber, *Kunst: Alter und neuer Meister* [Sale Catalogue no. 136, Nov. 23–24, 1973] (Munich 1973), lot 146, pl. 18.

2. This is also the beginning of the Gradual for the Vigil of the Nativity of John the Baptist (June 23).

3. Zacharias, whose presence is not explicitly called for by the biblical account (Luke 1:57–58), is compositionally derived from the figure of Joseph in the Nativity of Christ (cat. 3, 7).

4. *Corpus antiphonalium officii:* IV, *Responsoria, versus, hymni et varia (Rerum ecclesiasticarum documenta, series maior, fontes* X) (Rome 1970), p. 189.

5. See SISTER MINIATURE.

6. We wish to thank Professor Bertelli for his help with this and several other miniatures.

7. Giorgio Castelfranco, "I Corali miniati di S. Domenico di Gubbio," *Bollettino d'arte 8, no. 12* (June 1929), 529ff.

8. Otto Pächt and J. J. G. Alexander, *Illuminated Manuscripts in the Bodleian Library, Oxford: 2, Italian School* (Oxford 1970), nos. 91, 97, 107, 111, illus.

9. Hermann J. Hermann, *Die Italienischen Handschriften des Dugento und Trecento, 1. Bis zur Mitte des XIV. Jahrhunderts (Beschreibendes Verzeichnis der illuminierten Handschriften in Österreich, V, 1)* (Leipzig 1928), nos. 57, 65, 70, pls. XXX, 4; XXXV, 3; XLIV.

10. Domenico Fava, *Tesori delle biblioteche d'Italia: Emilia e Romagna* (Milan 1932), fig. 127. A mode of drapery modeling close to that in the Rosenwald leaf is found in the *Statuti dei Falegnami* of 1248. See Fava, 1932, fig. 126.

Fig. 4c. *Saint Nicholas giving Money to the Poor Nobleman.* Tübingen, R. A. Bohnke Collection

Fig. 4a. 1:1

5

Initial A from a Choir Book
(Antiphonary)

*The Three Holy Women
at the Tomb*
Central Italy (?), late 13th
century
B-18,760
267 x 219   (10 1/2 x 8 11/16)

Gothic minuscule script with four-line staff in red (25 mm)
CONDITION   (VG/E) Colors, although dull, are well preserved; only minor rubbing
PROVENANCE   Simkhovitch; L. J. Rosenwald, Jenkintown (1951); National Gallery of Art (1951)
EXHIBITED   South Bend, 1972, no. 8, illus.
SISTER MINIATURES
1) Formerly: Milan, Hoepli Collection: single leaf fragment (500 x 350 mm; staff 25 mm); the Nativity (*fig. 5b*).[1]
2) Philadelphia, Free Library, Lewis cod. M68.1: single leaf with initial I (560 x 332 mm; staff: 25 mm); monk with *aspergillum (fig. 5c)*.
3) (?) Cleveland, Museum of Art, cod. 51.549: single initial A (290 x 274 mm); Christ in Majesty worshiped by prophets (*fig. 5d*)[2]

RECTO   End of the Invitatory for Easter Sunday (with Psalm); followed by the antiphons and Psalms in the First Nocturn.
VERSO *(fig. 5a)*   Continuation of the First Nocturn; including the Response: *Angelu [s Domini] . . .* to (fragmentary) *. . . Sup [er] eum sedit.* (Matt. 28.2: . . . the Angel of the Lord descended from heaven, and came and rolled back the stone from the door, and sat upon it.)
    (Mark 16:1–7) The Angel, in a white mantle and dark greenish-blue tunic, sits atop a mottled brown sarcophagus. The three women (Mary Magdalene, Mary Mother of James, and Salome), approaching from the left with spice jars, wear overgarments of white, dark green, and blue, and tunics of dark red; the sleeping soldiers are in dark blue chain mail and red tunics. The background of the miniature is dark blue and the initial deep red, outlined in strips of uncolored vellum.

Fig. 5b. *The Nativity.* Formerly: Milan, Hoepli Collection (detail)

This initial, marking Easter Sunday, is one of at least three, perhaps four, fragments thus far identified as having originated in the same untraced Italian Antiphonary (the main choir book for the Divine Office).[3] Closely related are a series of eight single choir book initials sold in the early 1940s through L'Art Ancien.[4] Stylistically these fragments are difficult to date and localize, since they fall in the as yet little understood period before Giotto, characterized by the amalgamation in several centers of Byzantine and French Gothic elements (see cat. 3).

Pietro Toesca ascribed our miniature's sister leaf, formerly in the Hoepli Collection, to Central Italy.[5] Interesting similarities may be traced in an Evangeliary in the Biblioteca Nazionale, Florence (cod.

Fig. 5c. *Monk with Aspergillum.* Philadelphia, Free Library, Lewis cod. M68.1

II, 1, 167; from Santa Maria Nuova), assigned by Salmi to Florence, around 1300.[6] On the other hand, parallels also appear in an illuminated Bible in Oxford (Bodleian, cod. canon. bibl. lat. 56) written by Lanfrancus de Pancis de Cremona in 1265;[7] a Bible in Vienna (Nationalbibliothek, cod. 1127), assigned to Bologna c. 1300;[8] and in a copy of Boniface VIII, *Liber Sextus Decretalium* (Vienna, National-bibliothek, cod. 5043), produced about the same time in Padua.[9]

1. Pietro Toesca, *La Collezione di Ulrico Hoepli* (Milan 1930), no. XII, pl. X, 1.
2. William Milliken, "Style in Thirteenth and Fifteenth Century Illuminations," *The Bulletin of the Cleveland Museum of Art 39, no. 2* (Feb. 1952), 55ff., illus.
3. See SISTER MINIATURES.
4. L'Art Ancien, *Illustrated Books from the XV to the XIX Century* |Sale Catalogue: no. 26, n.d.] (Zurich, n.d.), lots 2–9, pl. 3.
5. Toesca, 1930, 21. Dr. Otto Pächt, whom we would like to thank for help with this fragment, also suggests Central Italy.
6. Mario Salmi, "Un Evangeliario miniato Fiorentino," *Rivista d'arte 19* (1937), 1ff. figs. 3–13. Compare especially the background ornament in fig. 13, and the head type and articulation of the hands in fig. 9, and fig. 5.
7. Otto Pächt and J. J. G. Alexander, *Illuminated Manuscripts in the Bodleian Library, Oxford: 2, Italian School* (Oxford 1970), no. 78, illus.
8. Hermann J. Hermann, *Die Italienischen Handschriften des Dugento und Trecento, 1. Bis zur Mitte des XIV. Jahrhunderts (Beschreibendes Verzeichnis der illuminierten Handschriften in Österreich, V, 1)* (Leipzig 1928), no. 36, pl. XXIV. Compare especially the winged dragons (Philadelphia leaf), and the fine white outlines.
9. Hermann, 1928, no. 22, pl. X, 3 (localized by colophon to Padua).

Fig. 5d. *Christ in Majesty worshiped by Prophets.* Cleveland, Museum of Art, cod. 51.549

6

Miniature from a
Laudario (?)

*Christ in Majesty with
Twelve Apostles*
Florence, c. 1320, workshop of
Pacino di Bonaguida
B-20,651
277 x 206   (10 15/16 x 8 1/8)

Staff: c. 26 mm; text block c. 206 mm wide

CONDITION   (VG) Colors bright and fresh; gold flaking; several areas
(e.g. lower left border) touched up; formerly glued to cardboard
backing; presently attached to protective backing

PROVENANCE[1]   C. G. Willoughby (up to 1929); B. Quaritch Ltd.,
London (1929–1951?); E. Rosenthal, Berkeley; L. J. Rosenwald,
Jenkintown (1951); National Gallery of Art (1952)

EXHIBITED   Trenton, 1971, no. 19

BIBLIOGRAPHY   Sotheby and Company, *Catalogue of Valuable Printed
Books and Illuminated Manuscripts* [Sale Catalogue: April 16, 1929]
(London 1929), lot 283 (C. G. Willoughby); Barnard Quaritch,
Limited, *A Catalogue of Illuminated and Other Manuscripts Together
with Some Works on Palaeography* (London 1931), p. 109, no. 159;
Richard Offner, *Corpus of Florentine Painting: Sec. 2, Vol. 6* (New
York 1956), pl. LX; Hartford, 1965, 44

SISTER MINIATURES[2]
1) New York, Pierpont Morgan Library, cod. M742: single leaf (450 x
333 mm; miniature: 256 x 207 mm; staff: 25 mm); Christ in Majesty
(*fig. 6b*)[3]
2) (?) London, British Museum, cod. add. 35,254B: single leaf
(440 x 320 mm); scene from the life of Saint Michael (*fig. 6c*)[4]
3) (?) Cambridge, Fitzwilliam Museum: single leaf (456 x 330 mm);
the Resurrection, the Three Women at the Tomb, (*fig. 6d*)[5]
4) (?) Formerly: New York, R. Lehman Collection: single leaf
(444 x 318 mm); the Ascension (*fig. 6e*)[6]

RECTO (?) (*fig. 6a*)   Christ, in a white mantle over a greenish-yellow

Fig. 6b. *Christ in Majesty*. New York, Pierpont Morgan Library,
cod. M742

22

tunic, is enthroned within a blue mandorla upon an arc of heaven. The twelve worshiping Apostles are dressed in garments of pink, orange, brown, and green. Peter is identifiable at Christ's right by facial type and preferred position; Bartholomew, patron of Florentine salt merchants, is identifiable at Christ's lower left by his patterned white mantle.[7]

VERSO (?)   Evidence of bar staffs and script (attached to protective backing).

In all probability this miniature was excised from a Laudario (vernacular choir book), at least four additional leaves of which are extant in European and American collections.[8] While these five miniatures (and three more to which they are closely related)[9] clearly betray the stylistic influence of Pacino di Bonaguida, the leading illuminator of early trecento Florence,[10] they are nonetheless distinguishable from products attributed to that master. The figures of the Rosenwald miniature, when compared to those inhabiting the rondels of Pacino's *Tree of Life* panel in Florence (Accademia delle Belle Arti, no. 8459),[11] show distinct facial types (lower foreheads with narrower eyes); a less clearly understood body structure; and generally less narrative and emotive expressiveness. These stylistic distinctions are also evident in relationship to a Morgan Library codex containing scenes from the life of Christ and of Saint Gerardo da Villamagna (cod. M643), assigned by Offner to Pacino, with assistants.[12] The Rosenwald fragment has a generally warmer color scheme with greener flesh tones. In addition, its pigments are applied more thickly, and its gold ground shows much more extensive punchwork.

1. Among our cutting's probable sister fragments is a leaf in the British Museum (cod. add. 35,254B) purchased from the John Malcolm of Poltalloch Collection in 1895. According to a catalogue of the Poltalloch Collection, the leaf was brought to England about 1820 by Abate Celotti, who stated that it was one of several leaves cut from books in the Sistine Chapel during the French occupation of Rome. See Richard Offner, *Corpus of Florentine Painting: Sec. 3, Vol. 8* (New York 1958), p. 200.
2. These leaves were all cut from a Laudario. They correspond in dimensions (of leaf and miniature), lay-out, and figure style. An association of nos. 1–4 was suggested by Offner in 1930. Richard Offner, *Corpus of Florentine Painting: Sec. 3, Vol. 2, Pt. 2* (New York 1930), p. 231. In his 1956 publication of the Rosenwald leaf (see Bibliography), Offner associated it with nos. 1 and 2.
3. Offner (Sec. 3, Vol. 2, Pt. 2), 1930, add. pl. VIII.
4. Offner (Sec. 3, Vol. 2, Pt. 2), 1930, add. pl. IX.
5. Richard Offner, *Corpus of Florentine Painting: Sec. 3, Vol. 2, Pt. 1* (New York 1930), pl. X.
6. Offner (Sec. 3, Vol. 2, Pt. 1), 1930, pl. XII.
7. George Kaftal, *Iconography of the Saints in Tuscan Painting* (Florence 1952), fig. 147. The four Apostles above the arc are probably Andrew, Peter, John, and James.
8. See SISTER MINIATURES.
9. 1) Formerly: Strasbourg, R. Forrer Collection: single miniature (175 x 210 mm); Adoration of the Magi [Offner, 1956, pl. LXXI]; 2) Rotterdam, van Beuningen Collection: single miniature (190 x 205 mm); Martyrdom of Saint Lawrence [Offner (Sec. 3, Vol. 2, Pt. 1), 1930, pl. XI]; 3) Formerly: New York, R. Lehman Collection: single leaf (470 x 350 mm); Martyrdom of Saint Lawrence [Offner, 1956, pl. LXV].
10. Offner (Sec. 3, Vol. 2, Pt. 1), 1930, pp. 1ff., 1f.; Offner, 1956, XIIIf.
11. Offner, 1956, pl. VIII (1–13).
12. Offner, 1956, pl. VIII (1–22); Meta Harrsen and George K. Boyce, *Italian Manuscripts in the Pierpont Morgan Library* (New York 1953), no. 22, pls. 3, 19 ("three artists"; "Pacino's atelier"). The Morgan Library miniatures are closer to the Florence *Tree of Life* panel than are the Rosenwald cutting and its sisters.

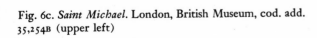

Fig. 6c. *Saint Michael*. London, British Museum, cod. add. 35,254B (upper left)

Fig. 6d. *Resurrection, and the Three Women at the Tomb*. Cambridge, Fitzwilliam Museum (upper right)

Fig. 6e. *Ascension*. Formerly: New York, R. Lehman Collection (lower right)

7

Leaf from a Choir Book
(Laudario)

*Nativity with the Annunciation
to the Shepherds*
Florence, c. 1340, Master of the
Dominican Effigies
B-15,393
365 × 271   (14 5/16 ×
10 11/16)

Italian: Gothic minuscule script with four-line staff in red (25 mm);
10 lines, 3 accompanied by staffs (c. 320 × 207 mm)

CONDITION (VG/E) Colors and facial detail well preserved; gold shows minor flaking; horizontal cut 67 mm from bottom; severely trimmed all around; minor water staining; evidence of slight retouching

PROVENANCE Conti Della Gherardesca, Florence; Sig. Bosi, Florence; H. Rosenthal, Lucerne; E. Rosenthal, Berkeley; L. J. Rosenwald, Jenkintown (1949); National Gallery of Art (1949)

EXHIBITED National Gallery, 1950, no. 9, illus.; Los Angeles, 1953–1954, no. 95, illus.; Hartford, 1965, no. 80, illus.; Trenton, 1971, no. 21; South Bend, 1972, no. 12

BIBLIOGRAPHY Richard Offner, *Corpus of Florentine Painting: Sec. 3 Vol. 7* (New York 1957), pl. XXI

RECTO *(fig. 7b)* An as yet unidentified *Laude*.

VERSO *(figs. 7a, 7c; Colorplate II)* Beginning of the *Laude* for the Nativity: *Xp[Chr]isto e nato [et] hu[manato per salvar la gente]*.[1]

This single leaf was once part of a Laudario or vernacular choir book with extraliturgical hymns written for use at the services of confraternities of lay persons (one of whom is visible in the lower margin). Some years ago Richard Offner attributed this leaf to the "Master of the Dominican Effigies," a prolific Florentine panel painter and miniaturist of the generation after Pacino di Bonaguida, named from a panel in the sacristy of Santa Maria Novella, showing Christ and the Virgin attended by seventeen Dominican saints.[2] The Rosenwald Nativity shows a number of similarities to the Dominican panel, datable after 1336,[3] and to the frontispiece miniature in the *Libro dei Lasciti alla Compagnia dei Capitani* in the Archivio di Stato, Florence (Or San Michele cod. 407), datable after 1340.[4] More striking parallels, however, may be found in two nativity miniatures attributed by Offner to the Master of the Dominican Effigies: Castelfiorentino, Santa Verdiana, Propositura cod. A (fol. VIIIv);[5] and Berlin, Kupferstich-kabinett, cod. 1228.[6] In the Castelfiorentino miniature precise counterparts may be found for: the spatially incongruous combination of stable roof and steep rocky landscape; the Virgin leaning against the crib; the tightly wrapped Christ Child; the adoring angels in the margin; the thoughtful Joseph sitting at the mouth of a small grotto; the announcing angel (pointing toward the shepherds with the right hand and the crib with the left); the first of the three shepherds; the dog; and the two grazing rams. Finally, the opening words of the hymns in both codices are marked by analogously colored and ornamented Gothic capital letters.[7] Similar parallels can be found in the Berlin leaf, which also shows the same characteristic type of tree, drawn with pen outline and colored with a green wash.

Fig. 7c. Verso, detail, 1:1

1. A. Tenneroni, *Inizii di antiche poesie Italiane religiose e morali* (Florence 1909), p. 88; Fernando Liuzzi, *La Lauda et i primordi della melodia Italiana* (Rome 1935), vol. 1, p. 330. We would like to thank David Wilkins for help with the text of this and the following Laudario fragment (cat. 8).
2. Offner, 1957, IIIff.; 28; pl. XXI. See also Richard Offner, *Corpus of Florentine Painting: Sec. 3, Vol. 2, Pt. 1* (New York 1930), p. 49, pl. XXV.
3. Compare especially the head of James of Forlì (Offner, 1930, pl. XXV²) with that of the Joseph in the Rosenwald Collection. While the facial types of this miniature are in some cases very close to those of the Biadaiolo Illuminator (compare Offner, 1930, pl. XVIII⁶ᵃ, and pl. XIX³), the figures and composition as a whole lack the emotive intensity characteristic of that miniaturist.

Fig. 7a

4. Offner, 1930, pl. xxix.

5. Offner, 1957, pl. xx[b].

6. Offner, 1930, pl. xv; Paul Wescher, *Miniaturen—Handschriften und Einzel-blätter—des Kupferstichkabinetts der Staatlichen Museen Berlin* (Leipzig 1931), p. 65f., fig. 54.

7. The square composition of the Rosenwald Nativity may have been adapted from a Nativity scene spread over a large initial P (*Puer Natus est Nobis . . .*, the beginning of the Introit for the third Christmas mass, the most characteristic location for a Nativity miniature in a Gradual). In such a format (used in the Berlin and Castelfiorentino miniatures) room is afforded in the area flanking the shaft of the letter for the shepherds and their flocks, which are squeezed in at the bottom of the Rosenwald miniature. Further, the three adoring angels, allotted to the margin of the Rosenwald leaf, are structurally integrated into the shaft of the Castelfiorentino initial.

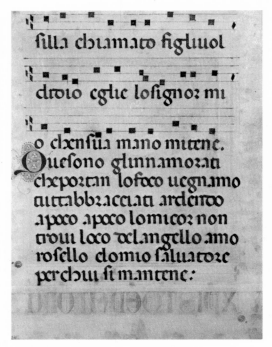

Fig. 7b. Recto

8

Leaf from a Choir Book (Laudario)

Christ and the Virgin Enthroned with Forty Saints
Florence, c. 1340, Master of the Dominican Effigies
B-22,128
409 X 311   (16 1/8 X 12 1/4)

Italian: Gothic minuscule script with four-line staff in red (25 mm); 9 lines, 3 accompanied by staffs (307 x 205 mm)

CONDITION   (VG) Colors and facial detail well preserved; gold highly polished but flaking in several areas, especially in marginal rondels; vellum ripped and restored at upper right (with a fragment from the same manuscript); verso text transcribed by a later hand; trimmed all around

PROVENANCE   E. Rosenthal, Berkeley; L. J. Rosenwald, Jenkintown (1956); National Gallery of Art (1959)

EXHIBITED   Hartford, 1965, no. 81, illus.

BIBLIOGRAPHY   Richard Offner, *Corpus of Florentine Painting: Sec. 3, Vol. 7* (New York 1957), pl. XVIII; Hartford, 1965, 45; H. P. Kraus, *Twenty-Five Manuscripts* [Sale Catalogue no. 95, n.d.] (New York, n.d.), pp. 51f

SISTER MINIATURES
1) Antwerp, Musée Mayer-van den Bergh, cod. 303: single leaf (430 x 330 mm); The Last Supper and the celebration of mass (*fig. 8c*)[1]
2) New York, H. P. Kraus Collection: single leaf (435 x 320 mm); Pentecost (*fig. 8d*)[2]

RECTO   Second stanza of the *Laude: Da l'alta luce fu dato sovente:*[3] [*Per nobil vita, alta reli*]*gione. dona Firenze di fedel doctrina et chi comprende la forte ragione. Che fece a decio di carita piena. com' è vertu quella che ciascun mena. a vedere incarnato idio con' fu m[en]ato. prenda dilecto et chanti allegramente.*

Fig. 8c. *Last Supper and the Celebration of the Mass.*
Antwerp, Musée Mayer-van den Bergh, cod. 303

29

VERSO *(figs. 8a, 8b)* Beginning of the *Laude* for all saints: *Facciam Laude a tutti [i sancti colla vergine magiore].*[4] The four figures flanking the throne have been identified as patron saints of Florence:[5] Saint Miniato(?) and Pope Victor I(?) (left); Saints Reparata and Zenobius(?) (right). In the three rows below, thirty-six saints appear, a number of which carry identifying attributes. Row one (from the top): John the Baptist, Saint Dominic, Saint Francis, (left to right); row two: (the twelve Apostles) Peter, Andrew, James, Paul; row three: Saint Stephen, Elijah(?), Lawrence(?), Lucy(?). In the marginal medallions the following figures and scenes may be identified: Christ flanked by the Annunciation (top; the Virgin medallion at the right has been substantially lost); Saint Agnes, Saint Lucy (left side); John the Evangelist(?) (right side); the Man of Sorrows flanked the Virgin and Saint John; and, between the medallions, a male and a female donor (bottom). The background of the miniature, as well as the mantles of Christ and the Virgin, are dark blue. Below, the saints are dressed in garments of green, bright orange-red, brown, blue, bright yellow and beige. The marginal decoration is blue and beige with accents in bright orange. Flesh tones are rendered in a cool grayish brown.

This leaf is one of three thus far identified as having originated in an as yet untraced Laudario.[6] Richard Offner attributed the miniature to the "Master of the Dominican Effigies," a Florentine manuscript and panel painter who is traceable in several dated works from 1336 to 1345,[7] and who acquires his name from a panel in the sacristy of Santa Maria Novella, showing Christ attended by seventeen Dominican saints.[8]

The single work within this artist's considerable oeuvre to which this last leaf most closely relates is precisely that Dominican panel whose *terminus post quem* is furnished by the 1336 death date of one of the depicted saints, Maurice of Hungary. Beyond compositional similarities, exact parallels of pose and gesture may be found in the panel. The Rosenwald Virgin, for example, is almost exactly duplicated, while the Apostle at the far left of row two finds a close counterpart in the figure of Saint Ambrose of Siena, occupying the analogous position in the Florence painting.[9]

Stylistic affinities may be traced in the panel[10] as well as in several manuscripts with miniatures attributed by Offner to the Master of the Dominican Effigies, including: the *Divine Comedy* in Milan, dated by colophon to 1337 (Castello Sforzesco, Biblioteca Trivulziana, cod. 1080);[11] a Gradual in Castelfiorentino (Santa Verdiana, Propositura cod. A),[12] the frontispiece to the *Libro dei Lasciti alla Compagnia dei Capitani* in Florence, datable from 1340 (Archivio di Stato, Or San Michele cod. 470),[13] and, the Rosenwald Nativity miniature (cat. 7). Both Rosenwald leaves show borders ornamented from the same repertoire of decorative motifs, and color schemes dominated by a flat, deep blue accented by yellow, yellow-green, brown, and orange-red. Heads are modeled with a series of soft gray lines following anatomical contours, and eyes have a fleshy fold beneath them, a muted brown shadow at their outer corners, and a pale green shadow on their upper lid. The hands, especially of the donors, are very similar, as is the artist's tendency to stack figures in a shallow pictorial space.

Beyond obvious links to Florence in the words of the *Laude* on the

Fig. 8b. Verso, detail, 1:1

30

FACCIAM LAVDE A TTVTTI

8a

reverse of the leaf (. . . *dona Firenze di fedel doctrina* . . .) and in the choice of saints flanking the throne, there is the conspicuous presence of the two Carmelite saints flanking the cross in the bottom row. Citing this evidence Offner suggested that the parent choir book was produced for the Company of Santa Maria del Carmine in Florence.[14]

1. Offner, 1957, pl. xix.
2. Kraus, n.d., [no. 95], no. 14, illus.
3. Fernando Liuzzi, *La Lauda et i primordi della melodia Italiana* (Rome 1935), vol. 2, p. 403, illus.
4. Liuzzi, 1935, vol. 2, p. 394, illus.; A. Tenneroni, *Inizii di antiche poesie Italiane religiose e morali* (Florence 1909), p. 110.
5. Offner, 1957, pl. xviii.
6. See SISTER MINIATURES.
7. Offner, 1957, 28.
8. Offner, 1957, 11iff., 28, pl. xviii. See also Richard Offner, *Corpus of Florentine Painting: Sec. 3, Vol. 2, Pt. 1* (New York 1930), p. 49, pl. xxv.
9. A comparable borrowing of figures, motifs, and compositional devices is evident in the Rosenwald Nativity miniature attributed to the Master of the Dominican Effigies (cat. 7).
10. Compare the bishop in the upper right medallion with James of Forli at the left center in the bottom row of the panel. See Offner, 1930, pl. xxv².
11. Compare the male donor at the bottom left with Dante on folio 36r. See Offner, 1957, pl. xiv^d. See also Peter Brieger, Millard Meiss, and Charles Singleton, *Illuminated Manuscripts of the Divine Comedy* (Princeton 1969) 2 vols., cat. 280, colorplate 1.
12. Compare the miniature of Christ in Glory surrounded by saints (fol. civr). Precise counterparts may be found for several of the Rosenwald figures. See Offner, 1957, pl. xx^f.
13. Saints Miniato and Reparata are closely paralleled by the angels flanking the Virgin's throne in this miniature. See Offner, 1930, pl. xxix.
14. Offner, 1957, pl. xviii. The significance of the prominently placed gold vase, and the large cross has yet to be determined.

Fig. 8d. *Pentecost*. New York, H.P. Kraus Collection

9

Two Miniatures from a Matricola

Saint James (A)
Saint Susanna (B)
Perugia, c. 1385
Matteo di Ser Cambio
B-14,987 (A), B-14,986 (B)
A 149 × 123   (5 15/16 × 4 7/8)
B 146 × 111   (5 3/4 × 4 3/8)

Gothic minuscule script; 1 column (?) of 21 lines (incomplete); column c. 120 mm wide

CONDITION   A: (VG/E) Halo moderately flaked; horizontal creases top and bottom (verso: R. Forrer stamp—Lugt suppl. 941a) B: (E) colors bright and fresh; numerous ink splashes (verso: name register extensively altered by several later hands)

PROVENANCE   Used for a number of years in a Perugia guild (Bv: names of guild members crossed out and substituted, one bearing a matriculation date between 1395–1399); R. Forrer, Strasbourg; J. Rosenthal, Munich (1931); E. Rosenthal, Berkeley; L. J. Rosenwald, Jenkintown (1947); National Gallery of Art (1948)

EXHIBITED   Munich, 1931, no. 16

BIBLIOGRAPHY   A. L. M., "Two Exhibitions at Munich," *The Burlington Magazine 59, no. 341* (Aug. 1931), 85

SISTER MINIATURE   Philadelphia, Free Library, cod. Lewis M29.11a: single miniature (146 × 111); Saint Michael (*fig. 9d*)[1]

A, RECTO (?) *(fig. 9a)*   Saint James, in a beige mantle over a dark blue tunic, stands beneath a light beige architectural portal symbolizing the *rione* or section of Perugia of which he is the patron saint (Porta Eburnea). He holds his attributes: in his left hand a book and in his right a pilgrim's staff and a wallet. He stands before a patterned curtain of blue and vermilion. The background of the miniature is

Fig. 9a. 1:1

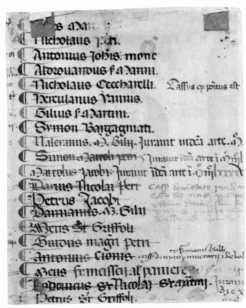

Fig. 9c. Verso (?)

dark blue; the frame deep green outlined in orange.

A, VERSO (?)   List of 21 guild members

B, RECTO (?) *(fig. 9b)*   Saint Susanna, wearing a bright red mantle over a dark green tunic, stands within a light beige portal (Porta Santa Susanna). In her left hand she holds her attribute: a shock of grain. The miniature's background is dark blue; its frame beige outlined in green.

B, VERSO (?) *(fig. 9c)*   List of 20 guild members with later alterations

These two miniatures, and another in the Lewis Collection, Philadelphia, were excised from a *matricola* (matriculation list with guild statutes) of the type produced during the second half of the fourteenth century for the various guilds and companies of Perugia. The decoration of such manuscripts might typically include a title page with the guild's coat-of-arms, or guild members kneeling before the Virgin and Child, and five miniatures representing the portals and patron saints of the *rioni* or sections of Perugia from which its members were drawn: Porta San Pietro (Saint Peter); Porta Eburnea (Saint James); Porta Santa Susanna (Saint Susanna); Porta San Angelo (Saint Michael); and Porta Sole (the sun).[2]

The illumination in a number of these codices is attributed to Matteo di Ser Cambio who signed the *matricola* of the money changers

Fig. 9b. 1:1

(*del Cambio*) of Perugia in 1377 (Perugia, Collegio del Cambio, cod. 1).[3] The style of Matteo, a goldsmith who is first mentioned in the matriculation list of his corporation in 1351, is characterized by sturdy, heavily draped figures with oval faces. While the Rosenwald miniatures show many similarities to those in the 1377 manuscript cited above,[4] they are even closer to their counterparts in a *matricola* of the stone-masons and carpenters, renewed in 1385 and attributed on stylistic grounds to Matteo di Ser Cambio (Perugia, Biblioteca Comunale).[5]

1. Hartford, 1965, no. 91, illus.
2. Walter Bombe, *Geschichte der Peruginer Malerei* (Berlin 1912), pp. 53ff. We would like to thank Gino Corti and Edith Kirsch for their help with the name lists on these cuttings. Unfortunately the lists, comprised of Christian names followed by patronymics, do not provide any substantial clues as to the nature of the guilds involved.
3. Mario Salmi, *La Miniatura Italiana* (Milan 1955), pl. XXIX. See also Bombe, 1912, 53ff.; Alberto Serafini, "Ricerche sulla miniatura Umbra (secoli XIV–XVI)," *L'Arte 15* (Feb. 1912), 54ff.; and Raimond van Marle, *The Development of the Italian Schools of Painting 5* (The Hague 1925), pp. 6ff.
4. van Marle, 1925, fig. 7.
5. Bombe, 1912, 56, fig. 30 (Saint James); and Serafini, 1912, fig. 13 (Saint Susanna).

Fig. 9d. *Saint Michael*. Philadelphia, Free Library, Lewis cod. M29.11a

35

10

Initial V from a Choir Book (Gradual)

Death of Saint Benedict
Florence, end of the 14th century

B-13,523
293 x 239   (11 9/16 x 9 7/16)

Gothic minuscule script with four-line staff in red (30 mm)

CONDITION   (VG/E) Colors fresh and bright with only minor rubbing; minor flaking toward lower center; gold tarnished and cracked; ink extensively deteriorated (verso: *865* penciled upper left, *23½ x 28½* penciled lower right)

PROVENANCE   E. Rosenthal, Berkeley; L. J. Rosenwald, Jenkintown (1946); National Gallery of Art (1946)

EXHIBITED   Munich, 1931, no. 12; Los Angeles, 1953–1954, no. 103; Trenton, 1971, no. 25; South Bend, 1972, no. 11, illus.

BIBLIOGRAPHY   L'Art Ancien, *Illustrated Books from the XV to the XIX Century* [Sale Catalogue no. 26, n.d.] (Zurich: L'Art Ancien S.A., n.d.), lot 29, illus.

RECTO *(fig. 10a)*   Beginning of the Introit for the Feast of Saint Benedict (March 21): *Vir [Dei] Ben[edic]tus.* (That man of God, Benedict, despised the glory of the world, and forsook it: for the spirit of God was in him.)

The single distinctive motif of Benedict's death as related in Voragine's *Golden Legend*, the vision of a shining road upon which Benedict was about to ascend to heaven, is not included in our miniature.[1] Instead, a simple funeral is conducted by a priest wearing a gray and black cope. Around the bier are gathered eleven monks dressed in the white habits assumed by two Benedictine branches, the Camaldolese (founded by Saint Romuald in the eleventh century), and the Olivetans (founded by Saint Bernard Tolomei of Siena in 1319). Two monks hold processional torches, one a bannered processional cross, and one an *aspergillum;* two kneel to kiss the hands and feet of the saint.

The patterned gold, beige, and red bier is placed on an orange floor. The initial, whose core is dark blue with orange and beige leafy extenders, is set against a highly burnished gold field framed by two rows of punchwork. The rubric for the mass is bright red.

VERSO   End of the Introit from the recto; followed by the Gradual (with rubric): *Fuit vir . . .* (with gaps to) *. . . abbas benedictus.*

This initial V, which marks the beginning of the mass for the Feast of Saint Benedict (March 21), is the only known fragment of an as yet untraced Italian Gradual. In general, it may be associated through initial format, border ornament, gold punchwork,[2] facial types, and drapery style with Florentine miniature painting of the late trecento.[3] More specifically this miniature bears comparison with the style of Spinello Aretino,[4] especially with his two versions of the same scene: a panel in the Fogg Art Museum, Cambridge, Massachusetts (no. 413), dated 1385,[5] and a fresco (part of an extensive cycle of Saint Benedict) in San Miniato al Monte, Florence (1387).[6] Parallels for the strange elliptical head of the fore-shortened monk in the center background are found in several works of Spinello.[7]

The Gradual from which this leaf was excised was very probably intended for a Camaldolese foundation. The leading Florentine monastery of that branch of the Benedictines was Santa Maria degli Angeli, which was also the leading center for manuscript illumination (to which belonged Don Simone, Don Silvestro dei Gherarducci, and Lorenzo Monaco).[8]

Compositionally, the Death of Saint Benedict is probably derived from the iconography of the Death of the Virgin (compare cat. 43), which is itself ultimately Byzantine in origin.[9] Because of the

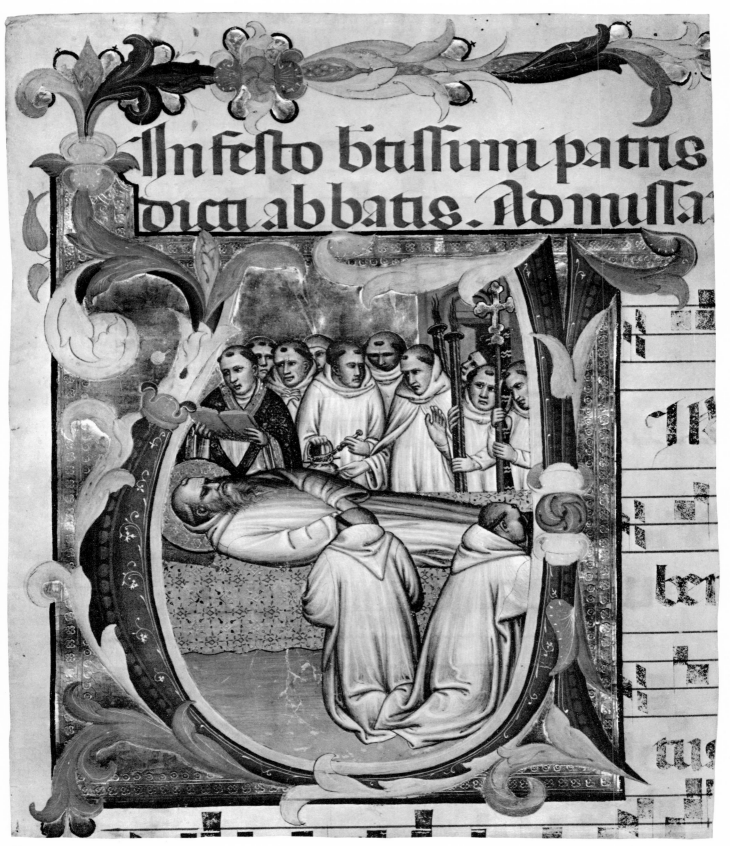

Fig. 10a

restricted space of the initial, the monk kissing the feet of Benedict is drawn around to the left, where he overlaps the other kneeling monk. Nonetheless, he and the feet of the Saint are covered by the shaft of the initial.

1. For a contemporary Florentine version of that iconography, see Paolo D'Ancona, *La Miniatura Fiorentina (secoli XI–XVI)* (Florence 1914), pl. xvii (Florence, Biblioteca Laurentiana, cod. corale 40 [San Pancrazio, cod. G], fol. 166v).

2. An *exact* parallel for the punchwork is found in a single miniature formerly in the Hoepli Collection. See Pietro Toesca, *La Collezione di Ulrico Hoepli* (Milan 1930), no. lxviii, pl. lviii: "Siena, second half of the fourteenth century."

3. See Mirella Levi D'Ancona, " 'Don Silvestro dei Gherarducci' e il 'Maestro delle Canzoni': due miniatori trecenteschi della scuola di S. Maria degli Angeli a Firenze," *Rivista d'arte 32* (1957, printed 1959), 3ff.; and Miklòs Boskovits, "Su Don Silvestro, Don Simone e la 'scuola degli Angeli'," *Paragone 265* (March 1972), 35ff.

4. We would like to thank Professor David Wilkins for helpful discussions of the miniature. For evidence that Spinello illuminated manuscripts, see A. R. Calderoni Masetti, *Spinello Aretino Giovanni* (Florence 1973).

5. F. Mason Perkins, "Una Tavola d'altare di Spinello Aretino," *Rassegna d'arte 5, nos. 1–2* (Jan.–Feb. 1918), fig. p. 1.

6. A. Venturi, *Storia dell'arte Italiana 5: La Pittura del trecento* (Milan 1907), fig. 700.

7. Including several sections of the San Miniato frescoes. See George Kaftal, *Iconography of the Saints in Tuscan Painting* (Florence 1952), fig. 166.

8. See note 3. It should be remembered, however, that the Fogg panel was part of an altarpiece formerly in the Olivetan monastery at Monte Oliveto near Siena. It was apparently commissioned in 1384 by Don Niccolò da Pisa, a member of that branch of the Benedictines which, like the Camaldolese, wears a white habit. See Perkins, 1918, pp. 1ff.

9. For a slightly later Florentine treatment of the Death of the Virgin, see D'Ancona, 1914, pl. xliv.

II

Initial S from a Choir Book
(Antiphonary)

*Christ Giving the Keys
to Saint Peter*
Florence, c. 1400
B-21,963
344 × 314   (13 9/16 × 12 3/8)

Gothic minuscule script with four–line staff in red (51 mm)

CONDITION   (E) Colors and detail very fresh and precise; gold highly burnished with only very minor flaking; penciled *913* (Rambout Collection signature) in lower right (verso: recent penciled notes)

PROVENANCE   Rambout (no. 913); Ducal Collection, Sigmaringen; E. Rosenthal, Berkeley; L. J. Rosenwald, Jenkintown (1955); National Gallery of Art (1958)

EXHIBITED   Hartford, 1965, no. 85; Trenton, 1971, no. 26

BIBLIOGRAPHY   Erwin Rosenthal, "Una Pittura di Lorenzo Monaco scoperta recentemente," *Commentari 7, no. 2* (1956), 71ff.; Marvin Eisenberg, "An Early Altarpiece by Lorenzo Monaco," *The Art Bulletin 39, no. 1* (March 1957), 51n.; Mirella Levi D'Ancona, "Some New Attributions to Lorenzo Monaco," *The Art Bulletin 40, no. 3* (Sept. 1958), 181n., 187n.; Luciano Bellosi, "Da Spinello Aretino a Lorenzo Monaco," *Paragone 16, no. 187* (1965), 39

RECTO *(fig. 11a, 11b)*   The last Psalm and Verse in the First Nocturn for the Feast of Saint Peter (June 29), followed by the first response: *Sym[on] Pe[tre, antequam de navi vocarem te novi te, et super plebem meam principem te constitui, et claves regni coelorum tradidi tibi]*.

Fig. 11b. Recto, detail, 1:1

Saint Peter, in a beige mantle over a bright reddish-orange tunic, is receiving his attribute (a pair of gold keys) from Christ, dressed in dark blue and rose. The lower half of the initial is filled with a carpet pattern of orange over dark green. The core of the letter S is bright blue, with leafy borders and extenders in orange, green, and beige. The background is highly burnished gold.

VERSO Second half of the Response begun on the recto: [*no*]*vi te et sup*[*er*] *ple*[*bem*] *meam pri*[*n*]*cipem* [*te C*]*o*[*n*]*stitui. Et.*

This colorful initial S, marking the first response for Matins on June 29th, the Feast of Saint Peter, was once part of a large illuminated Antiphonary. Although ties with the early style of Lorenzo Monaco have been suggested,[1] the miniature does not attain the quality of generally accepted early works (1390s) by that master, such as the *Agony in the Garden* panel in the Academia in Florence,[2] or the Saint Jerome(?) initial in corale 5 (dated 1394) in the Biblioteca Laurentiana (fol. 138r).[3] The structure of Christ's body is not clearly understood (especially in the lower half of the initial), nor is the relationship of the figures to one another, nor of both to the space of the initial itself.[4] The heavy, ungainly drapery of Saint Peter, as well as the facial types of both figures bear comparison with a cut-out initial O from a Florentine choir book in the Kupferstichkabinett in Berlin (cod. 1240),[5] and with the Apostles of the Ascension miniature in Florence, Biblioteca Laurentiana, cod. corale 1, an Antiphonary dated 1396.[6] A compositional prototype for the Rosenwald miniature may be found in an earlier Florentine Antiphonary in the Walters Art Gallery (cod. w153; fol. 4v-unpublished).[7]

While the facial types, drapery style, and initial ornament of the Rosenwald cutting bear comparison with Florentine choir book illumination from around 1400, it is difficult to make an attribution to any known master. Citing the late Orcagnesque quality of the miniature, Professor Marvin Eisenberg has compared it with the survivals of that style in works of the Gerini tradition and of Mariotto di Nardo and his shop.[8]

1. Rosenthal, 1956, passim.
2. Levi D'Ancona, 1958, fig. 22; Eisenberg, 1957, figs. 6, 9.
3. Levi D'Ancona, 1958, 189, fig. 20.
4. Citing these qualities Professor Mirella Levi D'Ancona (1958, 187) appraised the miniature as "a caricature of Lorenzo's style."
5. Paul Wescher, *Miniaturen—Handschriften und Einzelblätter—des Kupferstichkabinetts der Staatlichen Museen Berlin* (Leipzig 1931), p. 90, fig. 74 (as "Lorenzo Monaco"). In both the Rosenwald and Berlin miniatures the bar staff measures 51mm (We would like to thank Dr. Peter Dreyer of the Kupferstichkabinett for making that measurement).
6. Paolo D'Ancona, *La Miniatura Fiorentina (secoli XI–XVI)* (Florence 1914), vol. 2, pl. XXXII (as "forerunner of Lorenzo"). For a review of scholarship, see Levi D'Ancona, 1958, 188 (as by "a follower of Agnolo Gaddi").
7. Baltimore, 1949, no. 162.
8. We would like to thank Professor Eisenberg for very informative letters (May 23, September 7, 1974) regarding the Rosenwald cutting. According to a 1965 exhibition catalogue (Hartford, 1965, no. 85), Professor Mirella Levi D'Ancona suggested an attribution to Matteo Torelli. Dr. Miklòs Boskovits, who will discuss Lorenzo's chronology in a forthcoming book on Florentine painting between 1370 and 1400, generously communicated his opinion of this leaf in a letter of May 13, 1974. He attributes it to Lorenzo and suggests a date between 1390–1395. Luciano Bellosi (see *Bibliography*) also attributes the leaf to Lorenzo.

Fig. 11a

I2

Initial N from a Choir Book (Gradual)

Saint Peter Enthroned
Siena, c. 1420, follower of
Lippo Vanni
B-15,394
211 x 228 (8 5/16 x 9)

Gothic minuscule script with four-line staff in red (29 mm)

CONDITION (G) Gold extensively flaked and figure rubbed; vellum creased and wrinkled toward lower left; R. Forrer stamp (Lugt suppl. 941a); preparatory sketch visible beyond lower right edge of miniature

PROVENANCE R. Forrer, Strasbourg; E. Rosenthal, Berkeley (1949); L. J. Rosenwald, Jenkintown (1949); National Gallery of Art (1949)

EXHIBITED National Gallery, 1950, no. 8; Los Angeles, 1953–1954, no. 99

RECTO *(fig. 12a)* End of the Communion for the Vigil of Saints Peter and Paul (June 28): [*Do*]*mine quia am*[*o te.*]; followed by the Introit for the Feast of Saints Peter and Paul (June 29): *Nu*[*nc*] *sc*[*io vere,*] *qu*[*ia*]. (Acts 12:11: Now I know in very deed. . . .)

Saint Peter, dressed as a pontiff, is enthroned with his symbol, a pair of keys, in his left hand. He wears a richly patterned pink-beige chasuble over a white tunic: his throne is draped in a light red cloth covered with blue stars. The initial, predominantly pink with dark green and blue leafy extenders, is set against a dark blue background. The frame is light burgundy lined in dark green and red.

VERSO The end of the Introit from the recto: [*Judae*]*orum;* followed by a Psalm rubric and the verse: *Et Petrus* [*ad se rev*]*ersus dixit; Gloria* [*allel*]*uya;* and the verse: [*Tu es P*]*etrus et super ha*[*n*]*c pe*[*tram*].

This initial once formed part of a luxuriously illuminated Sienese choir book, where it marked the Introit to the mass recited on the Feast of Saints Peter and Paul (June 29). Stylistically, it is most closely related to an initial I with the figure of Saint Augustine in the Cini Collection, Venice (cod. 2066), attributed by Pietro Toesca to Lippo Vanni.[1] While the facial type, the over-all structure, and the vocabulary of vegetal ornament of these two initials are strongly reminiscent of Vanni,[2] they differ in several basic respects from miniatures by that master.[3] Compared to the broadly treated, robust figures occupying the initials of the so-called Berry Antiphonary (Cambridge, Mass., Harvard College Library, cod. Typ 79),[4] or the five miniatures attributed to Vanni in corale 4 in the Museo dell'Opera del Duomo, Siena,[5] the Rosenwald and Cini Saints appear soft and elegant. Their body structure is less clearly understood, as is the space they inhabit. Moreover, they show a softer, more decorative color scheme.

According to Dr. H. W. van Os, Lippo Vanni had a number of followers whose activity may be traced long after his death, in choir books of the Museo dell'Opera del Duomo, Siena.[6] Specifically, Dr. van Os has drawn parallels between the Rosenwald Saint Peter and the style of a pupil working around 1420.

1. Pietro Toesca, *La Collezione di Ulrico Hoepli* (Milan 1930), no. LXVI, pl. LVI.
2. Compare, for example, the Assumption of the Virgin and the Ascension, Cambridge, Mass., Harvard College Library, cod. Typ 79. See Bernard Berenson, "Un Antiphonaire avec miniatures par Lippo Vanni," *Gazette des Beaux-Arts 9* (May 1924), figs. p. 266, p. 270.
3. These observations are due to Dr. H. W. van Os (in a letter of April 18, 1974).
4. Berenson, 1924, passim.; *Illuminated and Calligraphic Manuscripts* (Cambridge, Mass.: Fogg Art Museum and Houghton Library, 1955), no. 45, pl. 24.
5. Raimond van Marle, *The Development of Italian Schools of Painting 2* (The Hague 1924), pp. 452ff., figs. 296–297. See also Raimond van Marle, "Cinque miniature di Lippo Vanni," *Rassegna la Diana 4, no. 2* (1929), 159f.
6. In a forthcoming article Dr. van Os will examine the atelier of Lippo Vanni, and will publish for the first time a number of the Siena miniatures.

Fig. 12a

I3

Initial E from a Choir Book (Gradual)

Praying Prophet
Florence, early 1420s, close to
Lorenzo Monaco
B-15,887
131 X 129 (5 1/8 X 5 1/16)

Gothic minuscule script with four-line staff in red (30 mm)

CONDITION (VG) Gold moderately rubbed, vellum wrinkled, floral border trimmed

PROVENANCE Santa Maria Nuova, Florence; by 1914 no longer part of its parent manuscript;[1] Simkhovitch; L. J. Rosenwald, Jenkintown (1949); National Gallery of Art (1950)

BIBLIOGRAPHY Mirella Levi D'Ancona, "Some New Attributions to Lorenzo Monaco," *The Art Bulletin 40, no. 3* (Sept. 1958), 177, 181, fig. 6

PARENT MANUSCRIPT Florence, Museo Nazionale, cod. H 74:[2] 225 folios (520 x 360 mm; 30 mm staff); Rosenwald miniature formerly located after folio 42 (old foliation) (*figs. 13c, 13d*)

RECTO (*fig. 13a;* Colorplate III) The beginning of the Introit for the first Sunday after the Ascension: E[*xaudi, Domine, vocem meam*]. (Psalm 26:7–9, 1: Hear, O Lord, my voice. . . .) This unidentified Old Testament prophet wears a prayer shawl over his head and shoulders.

VERSO (*fig. 13b*) The continuation of the Introit from the recto: *alleluia al*[*leluia.*]; followed by the Psalm: *Dominus il*[*luminatio*].

This Prophet initial was once part of a large, luxuriously illuminated choir book formerly in the church of Santa Maria Nuova in Florence, and now kept in the Bargello Museum (Florence, Museo Nazionale, cod. H 74).[3] For a number of years scholars have recognized the hand of Lorenzo Monaco, the most important Florentine quattrocento painter before Masolino and Masaccio, in the miniatures of this manuscript.[4] While early opinion tended to accept the entire decorative program as by Lorenzo, and to date it to his middle period

Fig. 13b. Verso

Fig. 13c. *Prophet* (fol. 16r; old foliation). Florence, Museo Nazionale, cod. H74 (detail)

Fig. 13a. 1:1

(around 1414, the date of his signed *Coronation of the Virgin* panel in the Uffizi),[5] more recent scholarship has assigned the codex to Lorenzo's later career (the early 1420s), and has begun the task of separating initials by the master from those by his followers.[6]

While the Rosenwald miniature is of undeniably high quality, it is not equal to the finest initials in the Bargello choir book, and, therefore, is probably not by Lorenzo Monaco himself.[7] The drapery, when compared with that of the prophet of folio 18r, for example, is relatively flat, the features only summarily treated, and the hands inexpressive.

1. Paolo D'Ancona, *La Miniatura Fiorentina (secoli XI–XVI)* (Florence 1914), vol. 2, pp. 138ff. does not list it in his description of cod. H 74.
2. Levi D'Ancona, 1958, 177, 181f., 190f. (with a review of scholarship), fig. 10. For further reproductions see Osvald Sirèn, *Don Lorenzo Monaco* (Strasbourg 1905), pls. 26–27; D'Ancona, 1914, vol. 1, pls. XLIX–L; and Anna Maria Ciaranfi, "Lorenzo Monaco miniatore," *L'Arte 35, no. 5* (Sept. 1932), figs. 3–10. The origin and original position of this cutting was kindly communicated to us by Mirella Levi D'Ancona in a letter of May 23, 1974 (she had originally suggested this relationship in her 1958 article cited above).
3. See note 2.
4. Sirèn, 1905, 71f.; D'Ancona, 1914, vol. 2, pp. 138ff.; and Ciaranfi, 1935, pp. 379ff.
5. For a review of this scholarship, see Levi D'Ancona, 1958, pp. 190f. In a forthcoming book on Florentine painting between 1370 and 1400, Dr. Miklòs Boskovits will discuss the chronology of Lorenzo Monaco's style. Dr. Boskovits considers the Rosenwald prophet to be by Lorenzo himself, and favors a date in the early 1410s (on the basis of similarities to the illumination in Florence, Biblioteca Laurentiana, cod. corale 3—for which he accepts the date of 1409—and the predella of the 1414 Uffizi *Coronation*). This information was kindly communicated to us by Dr. Boskovits in a letter of May 13, 1974.
6. Levi D'Ancona, 1958, 177, 181f., pp. 190f. Mirella Levi D'Ancona (who attributes the Rosenwald cutting to Lorenzo) favors a dating of c. 1423–1424 on the basis of similarities to the predella of the *Annunciation* panel in the Bartolini Chapel in Santa Trinità, Florence (which she suggests was influenced by Gentile da Fabriano's 1423 *Adoration of the Magi* panel in the Uffizi). Professor Marvin Eisenberg (in two very informative letters of May 23 and May 27, 1974) favors a slightly earlier dating of c. 1420–1422, choosing to separate the initial's style from the final works of Lorenzo. Further, he does not consider the Rosenwald prophet to be among those initials of codex H 74 by Lorenzo Monaco himself.
7. We owe these observations to Professor Eisenberg, who generously shared his special knowledge of Lorenzo Monaco (note 6).

Fig. 13d. *Prophet* (fol. 129v; old foliation). Florence, Museo Nazionale, cod. H74 (detail)

14

Initial I from a Choir Book (Antiphonary)

The Annunciation to Zacharias
Tuscany (?), c. 1400
B-14,961
221 X 147   (8 3/4 x 5 3/4)

Gothic minuscule script with four-line staff (29 mm; third line red)

CONDITION   (VG) Facial detail very precise; gold, although tarnished, is well preserved; pigment washed out in several spots along left side; horizontal wrinkles along right edge

PROVENANCE   E. Rosenthal, Berkeley; L. J. Rosenwald, Jenkintown (1947); National Gallery of Art (1948)

EXHIBITED   Los Angeles, 1953–1954, no. 102; Hartford, 1965, no. 104; Trenton, 1971, no. 18

BIBLIOGRAPHY   L'Art Ancien, *Illustrated Books from the XV to the XIX Century* [Sale Catalogue no. 26, n.d.] (Zurich: L'Art Ancien S.A., n.d.), lot 14, illus.

SISTER MINIATURES
1) Location unknown: single initial B (160 x 170 mm); Annunciation (*fig. 14b*)[1]
2) (?) Venice, Cini Collection, cod. 2115: single miniature (336 x 290 mm); The Annunciation to the Virgin (*fig. 14c*)[2]
3) (?) Venice, Cini Collection, cod. 2116: single miniature (171 x 280 mm); two scenes from the life of Saint Benedict (*fig. 14d*)[3]

RECTO   Psalms and antiphons at Vespers for the Vigil of the Nativity of John the Baptist (June 23) beginning with the Psalm to the third antiphon: B[ea]tus vi[r]. A[ntiphon] ... [co]ram domino et Spi[ritu] ... [reple]bitu[r] P[salm] Laud[ate] p[ueri]. A[ntiphon] ... [ant]e illum in spiritu. ...

VERSO (?) *(fig. 14a)*   Continuation of the Office of Vespers from the recto with the antiphon at the Magnificat: I[ngresso Zacharia templum Domini]. (Luke 1:9–11: When Zacharias had entered the temple of the Lord, there appeared to him the Angel Gabriel standing at the right of the altar of incense.)

Zacharias, dressed as an Old Testament priest in pale green garments, is depicted swinging a censer before the "altar of incense" in the apse of the temple. Gabriel, with purple tunic and wings, descends from the right. The architecture is blue-gray with red trim, the initial beige with elements in blue, and the background highly burnished gold. Transparent glazes are used in several areas.

Fig. 14d. *Scenes from the Life of Saint Benedict.* Venice, Cini Collection, cod. 2116

Fig. 14b. *Annunciation.*
Location unknown.

This initial is one of at least two, and perhaps four, fragments cut from an as yet untraced Italian Antiphonary.[4] Parallels have for some time been recognized for its thick drapery; expressive, painterly facial treatment; and illogical interior perspective in a miniature from a "*Liber Ethicorum*" in Berlin (Kupferstichkabinett, cod. 1233), signed by Laurentius de Voltolina, and attributed to the school of Bologna by Paul Wescher.[5] A Bolognese localization is also tentatively advanced by Pietro Toesca in his discussion of the two related fragments in the Cini Collection, Venice.[6] Finally, the gold arabesque ornament of one of the sister miniatures is like that popularized in the second half of the fourteenth century by Nicolò da Bologna, the most productive and influential Bolognese illuminator of that time.[7]

On the other hand, the facial types, drapery style, and general color schemes show many differences from Nicolò and his school (see cats. 15–17). Furthermore, parallels for several aspects of the Rosenwald miniature may be found in a choir book miniature in the Cleveland Museum (cod. 53.24), assigned by Mario Salmi to Abruzzi, "under Sienese influence."[8] Recently, several scholars have linked our miniature to Siena itself,[9] a hypothesis which gains support through comparisons to products of early fifteenth-century Sienese painters. Several predella panels of Martino di Bartolomeo de Siena, for example, bear comparison with the Rosenwald Zacharias miniature and its companion fragments.[10]

Fig. 14c. *Annunciation to the Virgin.* Venice, Cini Collection, cod. 2115

1. L'Art Ancien, *Graphik, Miniaturen, Zeichnungen* [Sale Catalogue, no. 39, n.d.] (Zurich: L'Art Ancien S.A., n.d.), lot 4, illus.
2. Pietro Toesca, *La Collezione di Ulrico Hoepli* (Milan 1930), no. cxv, pl. cxi.
3. Toesca, 1930, no. cxvi, pl. cxii.
4. See SISTER MINIATURES.
5. Paul Wescher, *Miniaturen—Handschriften und Einzelblätter—des Kupferstichkabinetts der Staatlichen Museen Berlin* (Leipzig 1931), p. 75, illus.
6. See notes 2 and 3.
7. Mario Salmi, *La Miniatura Italiana* (Milan 1955) pl. ix. A similar arabesque, as well as a comparable drapery style may be seen in the headpiece miniature to the *Statuti della Compagnia dello Spedale di S. Maria della Vita* in Bologna, dated 1408 (Biblioteca dell'Archiginnasio, Deposito Amministraz. Ospedali, cod. 4). See Domenico Fava, *Tesori delle biblioteche d'Italia: Emilia e Romagna* (Milan 1932), fig. 8.
8. Mario Salmi, *Italian Miniatures* (New York 1956), p. 36, fig. 51. In a recent exhibition catalogue it was attributed to Tuscany. See *Gothic Art: 1360–1440* (Cleveland: The Cleveland Museum of Art, 1963), no. 61, illus. In the Hartford Catalogue (Hartford, 1965, no. 57) it was associated with two other single leaves; attributed to the Master of the Beffi Triptych (by Federico Zeri); and assigned to the Abruzzi; second half of the fourteenth century.
9. According to the Hartford exhibition catalogue (Hartford, 1965, no. 104), Professors Millard Meiss and Mirella Levi D'Ancona both suggested Siena.
10. Compare, for example, the predella in the Philadelphia Museum of Art; the panel with the infant Saint Stephen in the Staedel Institute, Frankfurt; and the predella with an angel appearing to Saint Bridget in Berlin. For illustrations of the first two, see Bernard Berenson, *Italian Pictures of the Renaissance: Central Italian and North Italian Schools 2* (New York 1968), figs. 440–441. For the Berlin panel see George Kaftal, *Iconography of the Saints in Tuscan Painting* (Florence 1952), fig. 236.

Fig. 14a. 1:1

15

Leaf from Johannes
Andreae, *Novella* on the
Decretals of Gregory IX

*The Marriage; the Kiss of the
Bride (initial P); the Bride
Abandoned* (*initial D*)
Bologna, 1350s
Nicolò da Bologna
B-22,225
445 x 273   (17 1/8 x 10 3/4)

Minuscule university book hand; 2 columns of 74 lines (352 x 88 x 194 mm)

CONDITION   (E) Color and facial detail very well preserved; ink has deteriorated; 80% of left column once detached, re-attached and repaired; pentimenti beneath the feet of the bride in the initial P; occasional marks in the text by a later hand

PROVENANCE   H. P. Kraus, New York; L. J. Rosenwald, Jenkintown (1958); National Gallery of Art (1961)

EXHIBITED   Trenton, 1971, no. 22

BIBLIOGRAPHY   Gerhard Schmidt, " 'Andreas Me Pinsit,' frühe Miniaturen von Nicolò di Giacomo und Andrea de'Bartoli in dem Bologneser Offiziolo der Stiftsbibliothek Kremsmünster," *Wiener Jahrbuch für Kunstgeschichte 26* (1973), 63f., fig. 114

SISTER MINIATURE   Cambridge, Fitzwilliam Museum, cod. 331: single leaf (445 x 280 mm); Book v, *De Accusationibus (fig. 15c)*[1]

RECTO (*figs. 15a, 15b;* Colorplate IV)   Commentary on Book IV of the Decretals: *De Sponsalibus* (canon law of matrimony), consisting of three kinds of glosses on the text and three kinds of glosses on earlier glosses (note paragraph markings differentiating passages).[2]

The bride, and the groom who places a ring on her finger, are joined together by an older sponsor. To the left is the bride's entourage, including three crowned bridesmaids; and to the right is the entourage of the groom, including a man with a falcon. Music is provided by a violin, drums, and trumpets; spectators look on from an over-hanging balcony. In the opening initial P the bride and groom kiss; below in an initial D the bride stands abandoned, her left hand raised to her breast in a gesture of mourning.

Fig. 15b. Recto, detail, 1:1

Fig. 15c. Book V, *De Accusationibus*.
Cambridge, Fitzwilliam Museum, cod. 331
(detail)

This single leaf, along with another in the Fitzwilliam Museum, Cambridge (cod. 331), was excised from an as yet untraced fourteenth-century copy of the *Novella* of Johannes Andreae (c. 1270–1348) on the Decretals of Pope Gregory IX.[3] The facial types of its figures (pronounced nasolabial lines, prominent ears, and elongated eyes), as well as their gestures, the overall color scheme, and the format and ornament of the initials, warrant an attribution to Nicolò da Bologna.[4]

More specifically, the richness of detail, variety of gesture and pose, and the generally precise though energetic treatment link this miniature as well as its sister leaf in Cambridge with the earliest products by that master. They are especially close to miniatures in a Book of Hours in Kremsmünster (Schatzkasten, cod. 4), dated by colophon to 1349,[5] and to a Decretals manuscript in Salzburg (Benediktinerstift S. Peter, cod. a. XII. 10), dated 1354.[6] The Rosenwald leaf shows little hint of the broader, comparatively lifeless treatment that will characterize much of the stereotyped production of Nicolò's later career.[7]

1. Francis Wormald and Phyllis Giles, *Illuminated Manuscripts in the Fitzwilliam Museum* (Cambridge: Fitzwilliam Museum, 1966), no. 61; Schmidt, 1973, p. 63, fig. 115.
2. We would like to thank Professor Stephan Kuttner for helpful information regarding the text of this leaf. While there is no modern edition of the text, the 1581 Venice edition was recently reprinted: *Ioannis Andreae in quinque Decretalium libros Novella Commentaria* (Turin 1963). See Stephan Kuttner's introduction [reprinted in *The Jurist 24, no. 4* (1964), 393ff.].
3. See SISTER MINIATURE, and note 2. Johannes Andreae, the most famous and successful lay canonist of the medieval period, composed the *Novella* in his native city of Bologna (where he was professor of canon law) between c. 1311 and c. 1338.
4. The attribution was made by Gerhard Schmidt in his 1973 article (see BIBLIOGRAPHY). The Cambridge sister leaf had earlier been attributed to Nicolò (see note 1).
5. Schmidt, 1973, pp. 59ff., figs. 104–111, 120, 122. According to its colophon (Schmidt, 1973, fig. 104), that codex was written by the famous Bolognese calligrapher Bartolomeo de'Bartoli. Schmidt suggested (Schmidt, 1973, p. 63) that the Rosenwald and Fitzwilliam leaves were written by the same scribe.
6. H. Tietze, *Die illuminierten Handschriften in Salzburg* (Leipzig 1905), pp. 39f., pl. VI; Schmidt, 1973, p. 63, figs. 112–113, 116.
7. Compare especially the marriage miniature from a Decretals manuscript in Oxford (Bodleian Library, cod. canon. misc. 492). See Otto Pächt and J. J. G. Alexander, *Illuminated Manuscripts in the Bodleian Library Oxford: 2, Italian School* (Oxford 1970), no. 130, illus. Although Professor Schmidt suggested a dating in the later 1350s (citing a diminution in energy of expression and gesture), the Rosenwald and Cambridge leaves appear closer in their overall precision and vitality to the Kremsmünster codex of 1349 than to the Salzburg Decretals of 1354.

16

Initial F from a Choir Book (Antiphonary)

Birth of John the Baptist
Bologna, later 14th century
Nicolò da Bologna
B-15,392
258 x 225   (10 3/16 x 8 7/8)

Gothic minuscule script with four-line staff in red (52 mm)

CONDITION   (G) Gold and pigments show moderate rubbing throughout (especially blue background)

PROVENANCE   E. Rosenthal, Berkeley; L. J. Rosenwald, Jenkintown (1949); National Gallery of Art (1949)

EXHIBITED   National Gallery, 1950, no. 6; Hartford, 1965, no. 68; Trenton, 1971, no. 24

BIBLIOGRAPHY   Erardo Aeschlimann, "Aggiunte a Nicolò da Bologna," *Arte lombarda 14, no. 2* (1969), 35, fig. 19

RECTO *(fig. 16a)*   Beginning of the first Response in First Nocturns for the Feast of Saint John the Baptist (June 24): *Fui[t homo missus a Deo]*. (John 1:6–7: There was a man sent from God. . . .)

(Luke 1:57–58) Elizabeth, dressed in white and pale yellow, reclines beneath a blanket of dark red and blue stripes. The figure behind the bed wears deep red, while the women bathing John are in light blue (left) and pale orange garments. The carved headboard is beige, the background deep blue, and the initial a combination of pale pink, dark red, and green. The border ornament is predominantly light blue, with elements in pale pink, dark blue, and red.

VERSO   Continuation of the Response begun on the recto: *Hic venit ut [test]imonium*.

This initial F, marking the Feast of the Birth of John the Baptist, was excised from an as yet untraced fourteenth-century Antiphonary. Its figure style, initial structure, color scheme, and border ornament are closely paralleled in a group of choir books in the Biblioteca Estense in Modena, all of which were once in the Monastery of San Michele in Bosco at Bologna.[1] The decoration in those codices has been attributed through figure style and signature to Nicolò da Bologna. Among the eight choir books, the Rosenwald cutting is most clearly related to codex lat. 1023,[2] and to the codex lat. 1001, whose Birth of the Virgin initial repeats a number of elements of the present composition.[3] Although numerous choir book cuttings by Nicolò and his workshop are to be found in American and European collections, none has yet been proven to be a sister fragment to the Rosenwald Nativity.[4]

Stylistically the present cutting shows affinities with products of Nicolò's later career, such as the headpiece miniature to the Statutes of the Goldsmith's Guild in the Rosenwald Collection (cat. 17), datable to after 1383. It lacks the precise miniature style, and lively figures of Nicolò's earliest illumination such as that in a Book of Hours in the Kremsmünster Stiftsbibliothek (Schatzkasten, cod. 4), dated 1349,[5] or that of a Decretals fragment in the Rosenwald Collection (cat. 15), datable to the 1350s.

1. Domenico Fava and Mario Salmi, *I Manoscritti miniati della Biblioteca Estense di Modena* (Florence 1950), nos. 6–11, 13–14; pls. VII–XI; Paolo D'Ancona, "Nicolò da Bologna miniaturista del secolo XIV," *Arte lombarda 14, no. 2* (1969), 18.
2. Fava and Salmi, 1950, no. 7, pls. VII, 2; VIII; IX, 1.
3. Fava and Salmi, 1950, no. 13, pls. X, 4; XI, 1–2.
4. For example, there are five initials in the Free Library, Philadelphia (cods. Lewis 45.6–45.10; see Hartford, 1965, no. 71, illus.); three in the Kupferstichkabinett, Berlin (cods. 4187–4189; see Paul Wescher, *Miniaturen—Handschriften und Einzelblätter—des Kupferstichkabinetts der Staatlichen Museen Berlin* (Leipzig 1931), p. 73; twenty in the Poli Collection, Castelleto Ticino (Aeschlimann, 1969, 34, illus.); and two in the Cini Collection, Venice (Pietro Toesca, *La Collezione di Ulrico Hoepli* [Milan 1930], nos. XLIII–XLIV; pls. XXXV–XXXVI).
5. Gerhard Schmidt, " 'Andreas Me Pinsit', frühe Miniaturen von Nicolò di Giacomo und Andrea de'Bartoli in dem Bolognese Offiziolo der Stiftsbibliothek Kremsmünster," *Wiener Jahrbuch für Kunstgeschichte 26* (1973), esp. fig. 122.

Fig. 16a

17

Leaf (Headpiece) from a copy of the 1383 Statutes and Ordinances of the Goldsmith's Guild of Bologna

Madonna and Child Enthroned between Saints Petronius and Alle (Eligius);[1] *Christ in the initial A*
Bologna, after 1383
Nicolò da Bologna
B-13,659
356 x 210   (14 1/16 x 8 1/4)

Gothic cursive script; 1 column of 28 lines (220 x 164 mm)

CONDITION   (VG) Gold and pigments slightly rubbed throughout; worm holes near upper gutter edge; extensively trimmed on sides; (penciled) *200* in lower right; verso: marginal notes in later hand; (penciled) *31* in upper right, *15* in lower left

PROVENANCE   J. Rosenthal, Munich (1931); E. Rosenthal, Berkeley; L. J. Rosenwald, Jenkintown (1946); National Gallery of Art (1946)

EXHIBITED   Munich, 1931, no. 18; Baltimore, 1949, no. 164, illus.

BIBLIOGRAPHY   A. L. M. "Two Exhibitions at Munich," *The Burlington Magazine 59, no. 341* (Aug. 1931), 85, fig. B; L'Art Ancien, *Illustrated Books from the XV to the XIX Century* [Sale Catalogue no. 26, n.d.] (Zurich: L'Art Ancien S.A., n.d.), lot 16; Erardo Aeschlimann, "Aggiunte a Nicolò da Bologna," *Arte lombarda 14, no. 2* (1969), 35, pl. 14 (color)

RECTO *(figs. 17a, 17b)*   Prologue to the statutes and ordinances of the Goldsmith's Guild (*Societa degli Aurifici*) of Bologna according to the revision of 1383,[2] beginning: *Ad honorem, laudem, [et] reverentiam omnipotentis dei. . . .*

The enthroned Virgin is dressed in a blue mantle over a pink tunic; the Christ Child is wrapped in a red cloth. To the left stands Saint Petronius (mentioned in line 3 of the text), patron of Bologna. Portrayed as a bishop he wears a red cope over a white tunic. To the right stands Saint Alle (Eligius), a Merovingian Bishop who was himself a goldsmith and patron saint of all goldsmiths (mentioned in line 5 of the text). He is dressed in a pink chasuble with blue lining over a red dalmatic which in turn covers a white tunic. The throne is gray and the background deep blue, framed in red. Christ, below in a pink initial A, wears a red mantle over a blue tunic.

At the bottom of the page are three coats-of-arms. On the right is that of the Goldsmith's Guild: a gold chalice on a blue field.[3] The outer two are arms of the Commune of Bologna: (center) "France Ancient" (over-all fleur-de-lis against a blue field), labeled in red; and (left) a red cross over white, topped with a red-labeled "France Ancient."

VERSO   Completion of the prologue; statute: *De [Con]gregatio[n]e . . . ;* statute: *De Ellectore . . . ,* up to: *. . . m[in]istral[es] [et] ultra eos.*

This leaf originally marked the beginning of the statutes of the Bolognese Goldsmiths, as revised in 1383. Since its first exhibition in 1931 it has been attributed to Nicolò da Bologna (Nicolò di Giacomo di Nascimbene), an artist held in such high esteem that he was elected in 1393, to the *Consiglio dei Quattrocento.*[4] The saints flanking the Madonna, as well as the border ornament, and the Bolognese coats-of-arms find close parallels in two very similar frontispiece miniatures for statutes of Bolognese corporations both signed by Nicolò da Bologna: a single leaf in the New York collection of Mrs. Herbert Strauss,[5] and a codex in the Archivio di Stato, Bologna, dated 1394 (Compione Credit Monte, cod. 3).[6] The practice of heading corporation statutes with a depiction of the Enthroned Madonna flanked by appropriate patron saints (above Bolognese heraldic shields) was known in Bologna throughout the fourteenth century.[7] An exact iconographic parallel to the Rosenwald leaf is to be found in another copy of the 1383 Goldsmith Guild statutes in Bologna, illuminated by a follower of Nicolò.[8]

Fig. 17b. Recto, detail, 1:1

The Rosenwald miniature represents one of many commissions received by Nicolò later in his career from the Commune of Bologna.[9] These late works often show groups of rigid, frontal portraits with stock poses and gestures. Gone is the rich variety of precisely drawn, dramatically interacting figures of his early career, as may be seen in a Decretals fragment from the Rosenwald Collection datable to the 1350s (cat. 15).

1. Professor E. Panofsky originally suggested that "Alle" was a regional variant for Eligius.
2. Cyril G. E. Blunt, *The Goldsmiths of Italy* (London 1926), p. 85.
3. Blunt, 1926, p. 85.
4. Paolo D'Ancona, "Nicolò da Bologna miniaturista del secolo XIV," *Arte lombarda 14, no. 2* (1969), 1.
5. Aeschlimann, 1969, pp. 28f., figs. 12–13.
6. Domenico Fava, *Tesori delle biblioteche d'Italia: Emilia e Romagna* (Milan 1932), frontispiece.
7. Fava, 1932, fig. 149: *Statuto dei Merciai of 1328* (Bologna, Museo Civico, cod. 85).
8. Aeschlimann, 1969, fig. 36 (in the Archivio di Stato). On the adoption of the French fleur-de-lis arms by Bologna, see Comte P. Durrieu, "La provenance d'un des plus beaux manuscrits peints au XIVᵉ siècle par Nicolò di Giacomo da Bologna," *Bibliothèque de l'Ecole de Chartres*, LXXVII, 1916, pp. 120–121.
9. D'Ancona, 1969, p. 21.

18

Initial I from a Choir Book (Antiphonary)

The Nativity with Saint Bridget of Sweden
Milan, soon after 1391
B-18,761
197 x 122   (7 3/4 x 4 3/4)

Fig. 18b. Verso

Gothic minuscule script with four-line staff in black (second line red) (52 mm)

CONDITION   (VG) Minor rubbing and flaking (green shows moderate deterioration); flesh and drapery carry only very thin layers of pigment (verso: *54* [?] in brown ink, upper center)

PROVENANCE   E. Rosenthal, Berkeley; L. J. Rosenwald, Jenkintown, (1951); National Gallery of Art (1951)

RECTO (*fig. 18a;* Colorplate V)   Beginning of a Response for the Nativity of Christ (Dec. 24): *I*[*n principio erat verbum*]. (John 1:1: In the beginning was the word....)

The unusual iconography of this Nativity (compare cat. 3, 7) is based partly on the *Revelations* of Saint Bridget, a fourteenth-century Swedish princess who lived in Rome and who, on a pilgrimage to the Holy Land, saw a vision of the Nativity.[1] Among the elements of that vision incorporated into the miniature are: the presence of Saint Bridget in the left background[2] ("When I was present by the manger of the Lord . . ."); the Virgin's white garment ("I beheld a Virgin . . . well wrapped in a white mantle . . ."); the Virgin's blond hair (". . . her beautiful golden hair . . ."); the Virgin gives birth in a kneeling position;[3] the Child radiates light (". . . her son, from whom radiated such an ineffable light and splendor . . .");[4] the Child lies naked on the ground (". . . I saw the glorious infant lying on the ground naked and shining . . ."); and, the Virgin worships the Child (". . . she immediately worshiped Him, her head bent down and her hands clasped . . .").[5]

VERSO (*fig. 18b*)   Continuation of the Response from the recto: [*Ver*]*bum;* [*Hoc erat in*] *princi*[*pio*].

This single miniature with initial I was excised from an as yet untraced North Italian choir book. Stylistically it may be associated with the Milanese artistic milieu of the late fourteenth century out of which developed Giovannino dei Grassi, the illuminator responsible for the first part of the Visconti Hours (Florence, Biblioteca Nazionale, cods. BR 397, LF 22).[6] Specifically, it finds its closest parallels in the Adoration of the Magi miniature in a Book of Hours in Modena (Biblioteca Estense, cod. lat. 842) datable around 1390,[7] and in several miniatures of a prayer book in the Biblioteca Palatina, Parma (cod. pal. 56).[8] Especially comparable are the facial types (half closed eyes, pointed noses, wavy hair parted in the middle, wiry beards, and slightly open mouths with small, well shaped teeth); the prominent, cascading ridges of drapery with expressively curving hems (accented by contrasting linings); and the blond color scheme with its thinly applied pinks and browns, and strong dark blues and reds (and strong, though heavily deteriorated greens). Finally, the large radiating star of Bethlehem in the Modena Adoration is very close to the golden rays behind the Rosenwald Christ Child.

Although certain elements of this cutting conform to traditional Nativity iconography (e.g. the stable), and several of its innovative aspects had been anticipated in non-Bridgettine paintings (e.g. the radiating Christ Child),[9] it nonetheless is among the very earliest Italian Nativities to bear the imprint of Saint Bridget's vision of the Holy Birth.[10] Interest in the writings of Bridget, who died in 1373, reached a peak in the late 1370s with the distribution of a Latin "edition" of her *Revelations* between 1375 and 1378 by her last confessor, Alfonso de Vadaterra.[11] The Rosenwald miniature should

Fig. 18a. 1:1

probably not be dated before 1391, however, since Bridget is shown with a regular halo, an unlikely addition before her canonization, which was begun in that year by Boniface IX.[12]

Finally, a link to the great Milanese despot Giangaleazzo Visconti is suggested by the highly stylized aureole behind the Christ Child, a motif similar to the ubiquitous "Visconti sun" emblem of the Visconti Hours.[13]

1. *Revelations* VII, 21–22. For the text and a discussion of its influence on Italian Nativity iconography see: Henrik Cornell, "The Iconography of the Nativity of Christ," *Uppsala Universitets Årsskrift: Filosofi, Språkvetenskap och Historiska Vetenskaper 3* (1924), 1ff. (text appears pp. 9–13). For further discussion of Bridget's influence on art see: Carl Nordenfalk, "Saint Bridget of Sweden as Represented in Illuminated Manuscripts," *Essays in Honor of Erwin Panofsky (De Artibus opuscula 40)* (New York 1961), pp. 378.
2. Characteristically, she is dressed as a nun with white veil and collar. Bridget had founded a religious order based on the Rule of Saint Augustine.
3. According to Pseudo-Bonaventura's *Meditations on the Life of Christ* (dating from the late thirteenth century), the Virgin gives birth to Christ while standing and leaning against a column. A precise illustration of this passage is found in a fourteenth-century copy of the *Meditations* in Paris (Bibliothèque Nationale, cod. it. 115, fol. 19r). For both text and miniature see: *Meditations on the Life of Christ* (trans. and ed., Isa Ragusa and Rosalie Green) (Princeton 1961), p. 33. Structurally and functionally the initial I in the Rosenwald miniature recalls the column in the Paris codex.
4. The radiating Christ Child also appears in contemporary and slightly earlier Italian monuments uninfluenced by the Bridgettine vision: a triptych of 1367 in the National Gallery, London, by Giusto de Menabuoi [S. Bettini, *Giusto de Menabuoi e l'arte del Trecento* (Padua 1944), fig. 31]; a Book of Hours and Missal in the Bibliothèque Nationale, Paris (cod. lat. 757, fol. 109v), datable c. 1380 [Pietro Toesca, *La Pittura e la miniatura nella Lombardia* (Turin 1966), fig. 237]; and the Visconti Hours (Florence, Biblioteca Nazionale, LF 22, fol. 11r), begun in the late 1380s [Millard Meiss and Edith Kirsch, *The Visconti Hours* (New York 1972), LF 11]. We would like to thank Edith Kirsch for very helpful and informative discussions on the style and iconography of this miniature.
5. It should be pointed out that in several respects this miniature does not correspond to the vision of Saint Bridget. For example, the Nativity should take place in a cave, not a manger; Joseph should be outside the cave and a candle should be burning inside; the Virgin should be completely in white and her head should be uncovered. A more precise visualization of the Bridgettine text may be found in a panel in the Museo Civico, Pisa (see Cornell, 1924, fig. 13).
6. Meiss and Kirsch, 1972, esp. 13; and Edoardo Arslan, "Riflessioni sulla pittura gotica 'internazionale' in Lombardia nel tardo Trecento," *Arte lombarda 8, no. 2* (1963), 25ff.
7. Toesca, 1966, 159, fig. 319.
8. Angelo Ciavarella, *Codici miniati della Biblioteca Palatina di Parma* (Milan 1964), p. 42, pls. XIX–XX, 33–37; Analia Radaeli, "Di Uno sconosciuto codice Lombardo della Palatina di Parma e del suo miniatore," *Aurea parma 48, no. 3* (1964), 3ff.
9. See notes 3–5.
10. Cornell, 1924, pp. 15ff.
11. Nordenfalk, 1961, p. 379.
12. Nordenfalk, 1961, pp. 378, 382.
13. Compare especially BR397, fol. 61 with the Deity in the center of a blazing Visconti sun. See Meiss and Kirsch, 1972, BR61, and p. 11.

19

Miniature from a Psalter

Coronation of the Virgin with the Trinity and Saints
Milan, c. 1440, the "Olivetan Master"

B-18,754

157 x 143   (6 3/16 x 5 5/8)

Gothic minuscule script; 1 column of 6 lines (incomplete) (rule: 14 mm)

CONDITION   (E) Facial detail and modeling especially well preserved; several areas (e.g. Christ's tunic) show minor rubbing; gold rubbed and flaked; formerly glued to cardboard backing

PROVENANCE   Simkhovitch; L. J. Rosenwald, Jenkintown (1950); National Gallery of Art (1950)

EXHIBITED   South Bend, 1972, no. 9, illus.

BIBLIOGRAPHY   Mirella Levi D'Ancona, *The Wildenstein Collection of Illuminations: The Lombard School* (Florence 1970), pp. 17, 149; Ilaria Toesca, "In Margine al 'Maestro delle Vitae Imperatorum,'" *Paragone 237* (Nov. 1969), 74, fig. 48

SISTER MINIATURES

1) London, Courtauld Institute, Gambier-Parry Collection: single initial C (148 x 147 mm); David and Saints praising God (*fig. 19c*)[1]
2) New York, Pierpont Morgan Library, cod. M558A: single initial L (108 x 83 mm; staff: 42 mm; ruling: 15 mm); three martyrs (*fig. 19d*)[2]
3) New York, Pierpont Morgan Library, cod. M558B: single initial D (156 x 146 mm; ruling: 14 mm); the Baptism (*fig. 19e*)[3]
4) Paris, Bibliothèque Nationale, Cabinet des Estampes, cod. ad. 132 res., f. 32: single miniature; God the Father and a group of Olivetan monks (*fig. 19f*)[4]
5) (?) Philadelphia, Free Library, cod. Lewis M48.2: single initial H (?) (114 x 115 mm; staff: 40 mm; ruling: 14 mm); Saint Benedict (*fig. 19g*)[5]
6) (?) Florence, R. Longhi Collection: single initial G (95 x 118 mm); Saints Peter and Paul (*fig. 19h*)[6]

Fig. 19d. *Three Martyrs*. New York, Pierpont Morgan Library, cod. M558A

Fig. 19c. *David and Saints praising God*. London, Courtauld Institute, Gambier-Parry Collection

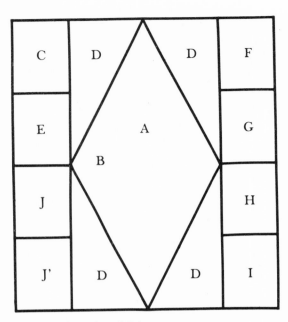

C	D		D	F
E		A		G
	B			
J				H
J'	D		D	I

Fig. 19i. Hierarchy of Saints

RECTO *(fig. 19a, 19i)* The choice, order, and rank of the figures depicted corresponds closely to the Litany of the Saints: A: The Trinity; B: Mary; C: Angels and Archangels: Michael, Gabriel, and Raphael; D: Blessed Spirits; E: Patriarchs and Prophets: John the Baptist, David (with psaltery), and Moses; F: Apostles and Evangelists: Peter, Paul, Andrew, and James (right to left); G: Martyrs: Stephen, Lawrence, and Vincent (right to left); H: Bishops, Confessors, and Doctors: Sylvester (?), Gregory, and Ambrose (left to right); I: Holy priests, levites, monks, and hermits: Dominic, Francis, Anthony, Bernard, and Benedict (dressed in the white Olivetan habit) (left to right); J: Female martyrs: Agnes, Lucy, and Catherine; J': Holy women: Mary Magdalene and Helen.

Christ, the Virgin, and God the Father wear dark blue mantles with green lining; the tunic of Christ is rose. The attendant Saints are dressed in blue and shades of red, from deep rose to bright orange red; there are occasional touches of green. The monks in the lower right wear habits of white, black, and light brown. There is liberal use throughout of tooled gold.

VERSO *(fig. 19b)* Part of the first division of Psalm 118 (i.e. verses 1–16), which is the first of four sections of Psalm 118 assigned in the Benedictine Psalter to be recited at the office of prime on Sunday (*Benedicti Regula* 18). Ps. 118:11–12 (119:11–12): *In corde meo . . . doce me iu[stificationes]*.

This miniature is one of at least four extant fragments of an as yet untraced Benedictine (Olivetan) Psalter. Judging from the text on its verso (Ps. 119:11–12), the miniature would have served as headpiece to the beginning of the extraordinarily long 119th Psalm, the first four sections of which are assigned in the Benedictine Psalter to the office of

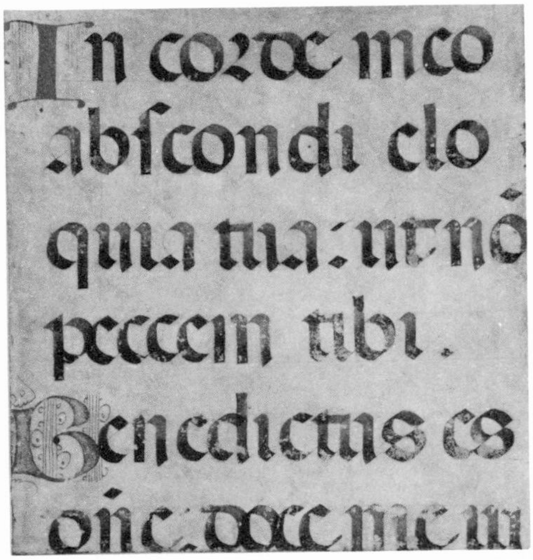

Fig. 19e. *The Baptism.* New York, Pierpont Morgan Library, cod. M558B

Fig. 19b. Verso

Fig. 19a. 1:1

prime on Sunday: "Blessed are the undefiled in the way, who walk in the law of the Lord. . . ."[7]

For many years the Rosenwald miniature, as well as its sister cuttings in the Morgan Library, have been attributed to the so-called Master of the Vitae Imperatorum,[8] a Milanese illuminator named from his participation in the decoration of a copy of Suetonius' *Vitae Imperatorum* in Paris (Bibliothèque Nationale, cod. it. 131), made in 1431 for Filippo Maria Visconti.[9] Recently, Alison Stones has associated the New York and London fragments with a stylistically identifiable subgroup within the oeuvre attributed to the Vitae Imperatorum Master.[10] At the center of that subgroup is a single miniature of "Christ as Pope, conducting Mass" in the Cini Collection, Venice, which carries the following colophon: *Q[u]id[a]m frat[er] mediolane[n]sis ordinis Montisoliveti opus explevit in* MCCCCXXXVIIIJ.[11] Although not cut from the same codex, the Cini miniature is nonetheless so close to the Rosenwald fragment as to warrant an attribution of the latter to the same hand (the "Olivetan Master"), and a dating very near 1439. That our minature's parent manuscript was in fact made for an Olivetan monastery (a reformed branch of the Benedictines), is proved by the fact that Saint Benedict, in the extreme lower right corner, is portrayed in the characteristically Olivetan white habit, not in the black habit of the Benedictines.[12] Close examination of the Rosenwald miniature suggests the participation of more than one illuminator.[13] Some of the head types on the right (especially those of Paul, Andrew, Benedict, and Bernard) show a freer, softer handling, and an expressiveness which contrasts with the rather monotonous, doll-like figures on the left.[14]

Iconographically our miniature is especially interesting in two respects. First, the choice, sequence, and rank of the Saints surrounding the Coronation of the Virgin corresponds unusually closely to their sequence as recited in the Litany of the Saints. Second, both in

Fig. 19f. *God the Father and a Group of Olivetan Monks*. Paris, Bibliothèque Nationale, Cabinet des Estampes, cod. ad. 132 res., f.32

Fig. 19g. *Saint Benedict*. Philadelphia, Free Library, cod. Lewis M48.2

this miniature and in its companion Baptism miniature in the Morgan Library an uncommon emphasis is afforded the Trinity, into whose midst, in this case, is introduced the Holy Virgin.

1. Alison Stones, "An Italian Miniature in the Gambier-Parry Collection," *The Burlington Magazine 111* (Jan. 1969), 7ff., fig. 8.
2. Meta Harrsen and George K. Boyce, *Italian Manuscripts in the Pierpont Morgan Library* (New York 1953), no. 52, pl. 43.
3. Stones, 1969, fig. 6. Alison Stones first suggested the relationship of nos. 1–3 in her 1969 article.
4. Toesca, 1969, p. 73, fig. 46. Dr. Toesca first suggested the relationship.
5. Unpublished. The Lewis Collection includes another closely related cut out miniature (M27. 19) showing Saint Ambrose in the initial H.
6. Toesca, 1969, 74, fig. 49; Antonio Boschetto, *La Collezione Roberto Longhi* (Florence 1971), pl. 164B.
7. The parent manuscript apparently included text passages written in two columns per page (e.g. the Rosenwald fragment) as well as music passages in one column per page (e.g. New York, Pierpont Morgan Library, cod. M558A) Judging from the ruling and script dimensions, and in view of the probability that the Rosenwald miniature headed Psalm 119, the parent codex may well have consisted of 2 columns of c. 14 lines (alternating with one column of 4–5 music staffs); with a text block of c. 360 x 310 mm and overall dimensions of c. 460 x 390 mm. Thus our miniature would have been located on the inside column of a recto page; the first ten verses of Psalm 119 would have been accommodated in the c. 36 ruled lines comprising the remainder of column 1, all of column 2, and all of column 1 of the verso.
8. This attribution is maintained in Levi D'Ancona, 1970, p. 15, p. 17.
9. For a general review of the Master of the Vitae Imperatorum, see Stones, 1969, pp. 7ff., and Levi D'Ancona, 1970, pp. 11ff.
10. Stones, 1969, pp. 7ff. For a review of Professor Stones' hypothesis see Toesca, 1969, pp. 73ff.
11. Pietro Toesca, *La Collezione di Ulrico Hoepli* (Milan 1930), no. XCIX, pl. XCIII. The Olivetans were founded by Saint Bernard Ptolomei of Siena in 1319. The Milanese Olivetan foundation dates from 1400.
12. Closely related to these miniatures is a single initial A, formerly in the Wildenstein Collection, showing Saint Benedict in a white habit, praying before a group of Olivetan monks. In the right background are shown three mountains with two olive branches and a red cross, the emblem of the Olivetan Order. See Levi D'Ancona, 1970, no. 1, pl. I. As Ilaria Toesca points out (Toesca, 1969, esp. p. 75), the Olivetan monks and symbols that are ubiquitous among miniatures of the "Olivetan Master" group, are not found in the "Vitae Imperatorum" group.
13. This was pointed out to us by Edith Kirsch.
14. The former head types recall the pathetic faces of Michelino da Besazzo.

Fig. 19h. *Peter and Paul.* Florence, R. Longhi Collection

20

Leaf from a Choir Book
(Antiphonary)

Annunciation to the Virgin
Lombardy, 1450–1460,
Belbello da Pavia
B-14,851
589 x 425   (23 1/8 x 16 3/4)

Gothic minuscule script with four-line staff in red; 5 lines accompanied by staffs (435 x 295 mm)

CONDITION   (E) Colors extremely fresh and facial detail very precise; off-print of bar staff across miniature

PROVENANCE   Drey, Munich; H. Goldman, New York (up to 1948); E. Rosenthal, Berkeley (1948); L. J. Rosenwald, Jenkintown (1948); National Gallery of Art (1948)

EXHIBITED   Baltimore, 1949, no. 179, illus.; National Gallery, 1950, no. 12; Los Angeles, 1953–1954, no. 104; South Bend, 1972, no. 23, illus.

BIBLIOGRAPHY   Parke-Bernet Galleries, *Works of Art Collected by the Late Henry Goldman* [Sale Catalogue no. 938: Feb. 28, 1948] (New York 1948), lot 73; Federico Zeri, "Belbello da Pavia: Un salterio," *Paragone 3* (March 1950), 51, fig. 17; Mario Salmi, "Contributo a Belbello da Pavia," *Miscellanea Giovanni Galbiati (Fontes Ambrosiani 26)*, 326; David Diringer, *The Illuminated Book: Its History and Production* (London 1958), p. 345; Renata Cipriani, "Belbello, Luchino," *Dizionario biografico degli Italiani 7* (Rome 1965), p. 546; Mirella Levi D'Ancona, *The Wildenstein Collection of Illuminations: The Lombard School* (Florence 1970), pp. 55f., 149

RECTO (*figs. 20a, 20b;* Colorplate VI)   [*sanc*]*tus est;* rubrics for the Psalm of the Magnificat; rubrics and the beginning of the first Antiphon at Vespers for the Feast of the Annunciation (March 25): *Missus est Gabriel . . .* [to] *. . . ad Mariam.* (Luke 1:26–27: The angel Gabriel was sent to Mary, a virgin espoused to Joseph. . . .)

VERSO   Continuation of the text from the recto.

Between the third and sixth decades of the fifteenth century, Belbello da Pavia illuminated manuscripts for three of the wealthiest and most powerful dynasties of northern Italy. Before 1431, Belbello completed for Filippo Maria Visconti, Duke of Milan, a Book of Hours begun in the late fourteenth century by Giovannino dei Grassi; between 1431 and 1434, he painted a Bible for Niccolò III d'Este, lord of Ferrara; and for more than two decades preceding 1461, he illuminated, for various members of the Gonzaga family of Mantua, a Missal to be used by their chaplain.[1] The Rosenwald Annunciation, unsurpassed in quality by the miniatures in these manuscripts, belonged to still a fourth kind of book, an Antiphonary, whose dimensions bespeak its use not by one person but rather by a clerical congregation during their performance of the liturgy.

In its radiant but quietly somber mood, the Annunciation resembles its counterpart in the Mantua Missal (fol. 269v). In both miniatures, God the Father is surrounded by refulgent angels in a night sky, and the position of His hands—almost identical in both paintings—indicates that He has just released the dove of the Holy Spirit. Other details shared by these Annunciations include the long, hollowed, and tapered wings of Gabriel; halos rendered in perspective; and a transparent veil beneath the mantle of the Virgin, gently falling onto her breast (and, in the Washington leaf, echoing the delicate contours of her face). Important for the dating of the Rosenwald miniature is the massive, unadorned wall behind the Virgin, similar to the parapet behind Gabriel in Mantua. Because Belbello's use of such simple, un-Gothic architectural forms occurs first in his later contributions to the Missal, a date before 1450 seems improbable for the leaf exhibited here.[2]

Still another portrayal of the Annunciation, now in the Giorgio Cini Foundation, but formerly part of an Antiphonary in San Giorgio Maggiore, Venice, has also been attributed to Belbello.[3] The Cini initial introduces the same text as the Washington miniature and seems to be derived both formally and iconographically from it and, even more, from the Mantua Annunciation. Like them, also, it is of high quality. The Cini miniature, however, represents a later phase of Belbello's career, more monumental and agitated but less lyrical than the moment crystallized in its predecessors.[4]

* This entry was written by Edith Kirsch.
1. For the Visconti Hours (Florence, Biblioteca Nazionale, cod. Landau-Finaly 22), see Pietro Toesca, *L'Uffiziolo Visconteo Landau Finaly donato alla Città di Firenze* (Florence 1951), and Millard Meiss and Edith Kirsch, *The Visconti Hours* (New York 1972). For the original attribution to Belbello of the Estense Bible (Vatican Library, cod. Barb. Lat. 613) and the Mantua Missal (Mantua, Palazzo Ducale), see Pietro Toesca, *La Pittura e la miniatura nella Lombardia* (Milan 1912), pp. 539ff. For the most recent comprehensive bibliography on Belbello, see Levi D'Ancona, 1970, pp. 56–59.
Scrutiny of the Mantua Missal in conjunction with the documents published by Guglielmo Pacchioni, "Belbello da Pavia e Gerolamo da Cremona, miniatori," *L'Arte 18* (1915), 367–371, indicates that Belbello worked on the Missal in three campaigns: before 1448, between 1448 and 1450, and between 1458 and 1461.
2. Federico Zeri (Zeri, 1950, 51) assigns the Washington miniature to the latter part of Belbello's career. Mario Salmi, on the other hand (Salmi, 1958, 326), perhaps because of its retrospective aspects, dates it shortly after the Estense Bible. The extensive nocturnal landscape, with hills, buildings, turrets, trees, and wattled fences etched in hold, is familiar from the Visconti Hours (Meiss and Kirsch, 1972, LF 109v). The Madonna seated on a tasseled cushion in a flower-strewn greensward evokes her predecessor in the frontispiece to the New Testament in Niccolò's Bible, representing the Virgin and Child together with Christ's ancestors (fol. 514). Furthermore, the floral and foliate rinceaux in the borders of the Rosenwald leaf recapitulate several forms in the margins of the same Vatican page. Nevertheless, the unforeshortened halos of the Vatican miniature, the swirls and loops of drapery which envelop its figures, and other mannerisms such as the Virgin's elongated hands underscore the evolution in Belbello's style apparent in the Rosenwald miniature.
3. Pietro Toesca, *La Collezione Enrico Hoepli* (Milan 1930), pp. 104–106; pl. 86.
4. Giordana Mariani Canova, "Il Recupero di un complesso librario dimenticato: i corali quattrocenteschi di S. Giorgio Maggiore a Venezia," *Arte Veneta 27* (1973), pp. 38ff., suggests the possibility of a date as late as 1469–1470 for the Cini Annunciation and other miniatures painted by Belbello for San Giorgio.
Several areas of the Cini leaf have been burned, probably by candles, and parts of the Madonna have been repainted. Perhaps the retouching was part of the seventeenth-century campaign of restoration discussed by Canova, pp. 38, 41.

Fig. 20b. Recto, detail

21

Initial D from a Choir Book (Gradual)

Saint Lawrence
Venice (?), 1440–1450,
"Master of the Murano
Gradual"
B-14,842
149 x 125   (5 7/8 x 4 15/16)

Fig. 21b. Verso

Gothic minuscule script with four-line staff in red (39 mm)

CONDITION   (E) Gold flaked in several areas, especially outside initial; colors bright and gold highly burnished; retouched in area of tonsure and grill

PROVENANCE   Czeczowitzka, Vienna; E. Rosenthal, Berkeley; L. J. Rosenwald, Jenkintown (1947); National Gallery of Art (1948)

BIBLIOGRAPHY   Hermann Ball and Paul Graupe, *Eine Wiener Sammlung*, II [Sale Catalogue, May 12, 1930] (Berlin 1930), lot 10, illus.; Paul Wescher, *Beschreibendes Verzeichnis der Miniaturen—Handschriften und Einzelblätter—des Kupferstichkabinetts der Staatlichen Museen Berlin* (Leipzig 1931), p. 110; Maggs Brothers [Sale Catalogue no. 642] (London 1937), no. 23; Mirella Levi D'Ancona, *The Wildenstein Collection of Illuminations: The Lombard School* (Florence 1970), pp. 55 (Czeczowitzka Collection), 56, 149

SISTER MINIATURE   The Cleveland Museum of Art, cod. 54.257: single initial S (168 x 149 mm; staff: 39 mm); bishop (*fig. 21c*)[1]
Note: The Rosenwald Saint Lawrence is closely related to a substantial group of single choir book miniatures, a number of which may have been cut from the same manuscript (see note 2). The fragments illustrated in *figs. 21d-21g* were formerly in the Wildenstein Collection and are now in the Musée Marmottan, Paris.

RECTO *(fig. 21a)*   Beginning of the Introit for the Vigil of the Feast of Saint Lawrence (Aug. 9): *D[ispersit, dedit pauperibus ...].* (Ps. 111:9: He hath distributed, he hath given to the poor....)

Saint Lawrence, dressed in a bright green dalmatic with a dark blue collar and white lining, holds a miniature version of his attribute, a grill. The initial is predominantly deep orange, with floral elements of bright green, light blue, and pale pink. The gold background is highly burnished.

VERSO *(fig. 21b)*   Beginning of the Communion for the Vigil of Saint Lawrence: *[Q]ui vult ven[ire].*

This miniature belongs to a group of cuttings attributed by some scholars to Belbello da Pavia and by others to one of his followers or to a related master, perhaps Venetian; dating of the miniatures has also varied, from c. 1434–1444 to after 1461.[2] Inasmuch as the Ottley sale catalogue of 1838 gives Murano as the provenance of one of the cuttings, from a Gradual, the illuminator of these leaves may perhaps, at present, be designated most precisely as the Master of the Murano Gradual.[3]

Although the Rosenwald Saint Lawrence and its affiliated miniatures share both formal and expressive qualities with the work of Belbello, the combination of these elements in them is improbable for the Pavian master at any stage of his career. In addition, the miniatures of the Murano Master display other characteristics which, while homogeneous to the group, distinguish it from Belbello's oeuvre. Several motifs in the Saint Lawrence, for example, are derived from Belbello's early illuminations. These include the gilt emulsion rinceaux on the burnished gold leaf behind the saint, as well as the floral pattern of his dalmatic, its bands of pseudo-Arabic script, and the contrasting color of its lining.[4] The ornamental quality which characterizes not only the deacon's vestment but also the overall design of the Saint Lawrence and its related cuttings tends, however, to disappear in Belbello's later works. (Certain calligraphic mannerisms of the Murano Master, such as the loop of drapery caught up in the

Fig. 21a. 1:1

Fig. 21c. *Bishop*. Cleveland, Museum of Art, cod. 54.25f

Fig. 21d. *Saint Augustine* (?). Paris, Musée Marmottan

bent elbow of the saint in *fig. 21f*, never appear in Belbello.) On the other hand, the emphatic plasticity of the head, neck, and hands of Saint Lawrence, like the fervor of his countenance, approximates Belbello's later miniatures, particularly his contributions of 1458–1461 to the Mantua Missal;[5] however, even the participants in Belbello's most ardent dramas—the Mantua Pentecost and Assumption of the Virgin, for example—do not attain the same kind of emotional gravity as the figures of the Murano Master. Vestiges of the humor and occasional caricature of the Visconti Hours persist in Belbello's late painting, though transposed into a far more serious mode.[6] Furthermore, although Belbello's concern with volume increased conspicuously during his long career, the faces of the Murano Master tend consistently to be broader and more powerfully modeled than his. Their brows are craggier, their lips thicker, their ears more hollow and more structurally articulated, their noses more prominent and frequently aquiline. The Murano Master shares only to a limited degree Belbello's fascination with the flow of silky hair and the activity of its individual strands, and he often imparts to it instead the wiry chunkiness of Saint Lawrence's locks.

The identity of the Saint Lawrence illuminator remains uncertain, though a personality begins to emerge. Circumstantial evidence points to his extensive activity in Venice, and a lengthy sojourn there could account for Venetian elements in a style which is not, on the whole, characteristic of that city.[7] His association with San Michele in Murano may also explain the Florentine aspect of the beaded, veined, and filigreed acanthus and palmettes of the master's initials. Vasari and other sources indicate that during the fourteenth and early fifteenth centuries, celebrated illuminators from the Camaldolese monastery of Santa Maria degli Angeli in Florence painted numerous choir books for San Michele and for its sister foundation, San Mattia in Murano.[8] Such highly prized volumes would surely have been known to any later illuminator employed by the Venetian congregation. The most salient affinities of the Murano Master's work, however, are with Lombard illumination and particularly with the miniatures of Belbello da Pavia. On at least two occasions, both masters seem to have painted in the same manuscript. The Murano Master's contribution to the earliest surviving major commission of Belbello, the Visconti Hours, includes the portraits on folio 57 verso of the second volume of that manuscript.[9] The Saint Justine among the Wildenstein-Marmottan cuttings, on the other hand, may be a later work by Belbello, painted in Venice under the influence of the Murano Master.

Because the distinctive qualities of the Murano Master are less developed in the Visconti Hours than in the Saint Lawrence group, the former would seem to have been painted earlier. The cuttings, furthermore, presuppose not only the Visconti manuscript but also the Bible painted by Belbello for Niccolò III d'Este before 1434.[10] The ornamental nature of the Saint Lawrence and its most closely related miniatures, however, as well as the absence in them of prominently articulated form beneath the drapery, points to a date before the middle of the century.[11]

* This entry was written by Edith Kirsch, to whom we are especially grateful. We would also like to thank Dr. J. J. G. Alexander for a very informative letter (Sept. 1973) regarding this miniature.

Fig. 21e. *Saint Margaret*. Paris, Musée Marmottan

Fig. 21f. *Unidentified Saint*. Paris, Musée Marmottan

1. Paolo D'Ancona and Erardo Aeschlimann, *The Art of Illumination* (London 1969), pl. 130.

2. The nucleus of the group, a full-page miniature representing the Descent of the Holy Spirit, and eleven initials, each portraying a saint, was first published by Amadée Boinet, *La Collection de miniatures de M. Edouard Kann* (Paris 1926), pp. 27ff., pls. XXVII–XXXIII. Boinet, who suggested that the Descent of the Holy Spirit had been painted by Belbello, attributed the initials less specifically to the Lombard school of the mid-fifteenth century. He stated, however, that all the cuttings had belonged to the same manuscript, an assertion which, though unexplained by Boinet, is supported by stylistic similarities. Because the miniatures are now pasted down, examination of their versos is impossible. The possibility of a common provenance is, however, further indicated by L. Sotheby, *Catalogue of . . . Miniature Paintings . . . of . . . William Young Ottley* [Sale Catalogue: May 11, 1838] (London 1838). Here, Murano appears as the provenance not only of the Death of the Virgin (no. 191) and the Descent of the Holy Spirit (no. 192) but also of nine other lots (nos. 31–39) of fourteen miniatures, the latter all attributed to the same hand. Some of these, described simply as "bishop," "male saint," or "female saint," could refer to the Kann initials, which, together with the Descent of the Holy Spirit, later entered the collection of Georges Wildenstein and were recently given by M. Daniel Wildenstein to the French Académie des Beaux-Arts for display in the Musée Marmottan. The Death of the Virgin is now in the Fitzwilliam Museum [Francis Wormald and Phyllis Giles, *Illuminated Manuscripts in the Fitzwilliam Museum* (Cambridge 1966), no. 89]. If, as Mirella Levi D'Ancona suggests (Levi D'Ancona, 1970, p. 42), these cuttings came from the Camaldolese monastery of San Michele in Murano, which was plundered by the army of Napoleon I, the appearance of the miniatures on the market in 1838 would not be surprising.

Pietro Toesca [*La Collezione Enrico Hoepli* (Milan 1930), p. 94n.] identified the author of the Kann cuttings (except Saint Justine of Padua, which he omits but does not discuss) as a follower of Belbello who also illuminated several miniatures in an Antiphonary in Berlin (Kupferstichkabinett, cod. 78 F 1), written, according to the Litanies, for a Camaldolese foundation in Venice. [For the Venetian and Camaldolese provenance of this manuscript, see also H. Boese, *Die Lateinischen Handschriften der Sammlung Hamilton zu Berlin* (Wiesbaden 1966), no. 29. Boese, however, erroneously states that the Antiphonary was made in Florence in the late fourteenth century.] Toesca attributed to the same painter three miniatures in the Holford Collection [Robert Benson, *The Holford Collection, Dorchester House* (London 1927), vol. 1, nos. 27a–c]. Paul Wescher (Wescher, 1931, p. 110f.) also ascribes to Venice in the first half of the fifteenth century the Berlin Antiphonary and the Kann and Holford cuttings, as well as the Saint Lawrence (now Rosenwald) and two additional miniatures, one of the Birth of the Baptist and the other of four saints, both formerly in the Marczell de Nemes Collection [W. M. Mensing, Sale Catalogue: Nov. 13–14, 1928] (Amsterdam 1928), nos. 97, 98, both illus. (The cutting of the four saints is now in New York, The Metropolitan Museum, no. 48–40.) Wescher also attributes to this master (erroneously in our opinion) the Annunciation and the Martyrdom of Saint Stephen now in the Cini Foundation (Toesca, 1930, pls. LXXXVI, LXXXVII). Mario Salmi ["Contributo a Belbello da Pavia," *Miscellanea Giovanni Galbiati (Fontes Ambrosiani 26)* (Milan 1951), p. 325] assigns all the Wildenstein (formerly Kann) cuttings to Belbello himself, dates them 1434–1444, and proposes that they demonstrate the influence of Lorenzo Monaco on the Pavian illuminator. Professor Levi D'Ancona (Levi D'Ancona, 1970, 37f.) accepts the attribution to Belbello but dates the miniatures about 1462. Finally, in his review of *The Art of Illumination* (D'Ancona and Aeschlimann, 1969), J. J. G. Alexander [*The Burlington Magazine 112* (April 1970), 112] rejects the attribution to Belbello of the Berlin Antiphonary and other works associated with it by Wescher, and ascribes them instead to "an anonymous artist, possibly Venetian."

Other miniatures belonging to the Saint Lawrence group (only those known to the author are listed) include:

Bern, Estate of L. C. Randall (formerly New York, Hirsch Estate). Saint Jerome [Millard Meiss, "An Early Lombard Altarpiece," *Arte Antica e Moderna* (1961), 132 n. 28].

Boston, Museum of Fine Arts, no. 1973-692 (formerly New York, Hirsch Estate). Vision of Saint Romuald. Meiss, 1961, 132 n. 28 and fig. 10, calls attention to the rarity of the scene—further evidence that the illuminator worked for a Camaldolese foundation.

St. Louis Art Museum, no. 36:53. Crucifixion of Saint Andrew. Reproduced in Karl and Faber [Sale Catalogue No. 35: Nov. 9–10, 1950] (Munich 1950), no. 1381, pl. IV.

Whereabouts unknown (formerly New York, Hirsch Estate). Saint Michael (Meiss, 1961, 132 n. 28).

Fig. 21g. *Saint Stephan*. Paris, Musée Marmottan

For the contribution of the Murano Master to the Visconti Hours, see below.

3. For the Ottley catalogue, see above, note 2.

4. Compare, for example, Belbello's miniatures of before 1431 in the Visconti Hours (Florence, Biblioteca Nazionale, cod. Landau-Finaly 22), folios 47, 79, 147 verso, 155 [Millard Meiss and Edith Kirsch, *The Visconti Hours* (New York 1972)].

5. Mantua, Palazzo Ducale. For documents concerning the date of this manuscript see Guglielmo Pacchioni, "Belbello da Pavia e Gerolamo da Cremona, miniatori," *L'Arte 18* (1915), 367–371. Three phases of Belbello's work are discernible in the Missal, the last dating from 1458–1461.

6. Compare the Mantua Pentecost and Assumption of the Virgin [Pietro Toesca, *La pittura e la miniatura nella Lombardia* (2nd ed., Turin 1966), figs. 484, 483] with the Wildenstein Descent of the Holy Spirit (Levi D'Ancona, 1970, pl. IV).

7. For evidence demonstrating the Murano Master's association with Venice, see above, note 2. For Venetian components in the style of the master, see Levi D'Ancona, 1970, pp. 37, 42, 49 (no. 13). Giordana Mariani Canova ["Il Recupero di un complesso librario dimenticato: i corali quattrocenteschi di S. Giorgio Maggiore a Venezia," *Arte Veneta 27* (1973), 38–64] discusses the employment of Belbello and other Lombard illuminators by the Benedictine monastery of S. Giorgio Maggiore in Venice during the second half of the fifteenth century.

8. Vasari-Milanesi, vol. 2, 1878, pp. 22f.; Vittorio Meneghin, *S. Michele in Isola di Venezia* (Venice 1962), vol. 1, pp. 111f.

9. Meiss and Kirsch, 1972, LF 57 verso. Professor Levi D'Ancona (Levi D'Ancona, 1970, 37f.) indicates an identity of authorship in 57 verso and the Wildenstein miniatures. She attributes both, however, to Belbello himself after 1461.

10. Rome, Biblioteca Vaticana, cod. Barb. Lat. 613. On April 10, 1434, Jacopino d'Arezzo was paid for completion of the Bible [Hermann Julius Hermann, "Zur Geschichte der Miniaturmalerei am Hofe der Este in Ferrara," *Jahrbuch der Kunsthistorischen Sammlungen des Allerhöchsten Kaiserhauses 21* (1900), 247]. The Saint Jerome in the frontispiece (folio 1) of the Estense Bible (Toesca, 1966, fig. 488) is the antecedent of one of the apostles in the Wildenstein Descent of the Holy Spirit (Levi D'Ancona, 1970, pl. IV).

11. The style of the Murano Master, like Belbello's, seems to have evolved over many years. The Fitzwilliam Death of the Virgin (see above, note 2) suggests recent familiarity with the Visconti Hours. The Boston Saint Romuald, at the other extreme, may be a late work of the Murano Master, reflecting in its draperies—still heavy and calligraphic, but now etherealizing the figures they clothe—the style of Belbello around 1460.

Serena Boskovits Padovani will soon publish a study relating the Murano Master to the Master of the Vignola (Rocca) and Carpi (Sagra) fresco cycles.

22

Initial A from a Choir Book (Antiphonary)

Saint Maurice and the Theban Legion
Lombardy, third quarter 15th century
B-15,395
143–203 X 141–186
(5 5/8–8 x 5 9/16–7 5/16)

Gothic minuscule script accompanied by four-line staff in red (37 mm)

CONDITION (G) Minor rubbing and flaking throughout; gold cracked and tarnished; silver heavily tarnished; pentimenti of Maurice's staff; formerly pasted to cardboard backing

PROVENANCE Como Cathedral; Lady Northwick; Czeczowitzka Collection, Vienna (1930); E. Rosenthal, Berkeley; L. J. Rosenwald, Jenkintown (1949); National Gallery of Art (1949)

EXHIBITED National Gallery, 1950, no. 13; Trenton, 1971, no. 34

BIBLIOGRAPHY Hermann Ball and Paule Graupe, *Eine Wiener Sammlung 2* [Sale Catalogue, May 12, 1930] (Berlin 1930) lot 12, illus.; Paul Wescher, *Miniaturen-Handschriften und Einzelblätter—des Kupferstichkabinetts der Staatlichen Museen Berlin* (Leipzig 1931), p. 124 (Czeczowitzka Collection); Mirella Levi D'Ancona, *The Wildenstein Collection of Illuminations: The Lombard School* (Florence 1970), p. 17 (Czeczowitzka Collection)

SISTER MINIATURE Formerly: Vienna, Czeczowitzka Collection: single initial U (140 x 150 mm); Saint Ursula and her maidens (*fig. 22c*)[1]

RECTO (*fig. 22a*) Beginning of the first Antiphon at First Nocturns for the Feast of Saint Maurice and his Companions (Sept. 22): *A[bsterget Deus omnem lacrimam]*.

Saint Maurice and his companions were soldiers of the Theban Legion of the Roman Army stationed in Octodurum (modern Martigny) on the Rhone above Lake Geneva. When Emperor Maximian (c. 287) issued an order that the army sacrifice to the Roman gods, the Theban Legion withdrew, refusing to take part in the sacrifice. They were consequently beheaded by Maximian and were regarded as martyrs by the early Christians.

All soldiers are dressed in (heavily tarnished) silver armor; Maurice, holding a mace and a bannered staff, wears an orange surcoat with a red cross. The dark greenish-brown earth is highlighted in gold; the sky is shaded from nearly white at the horizon to deep blue near the top. The body of the initial is rose with vegetal extenders in dark blue and dark green. The right shaft of the letter bears the inscription: *S[anctus] Mauriti[us]*.

VERSO (*fig. 22b*) Continuation of the antiphon from the recto: *neq[ue luctus, necque clamor, se]d nec ullus do[lor]*.

Fig. 22b. Verso

The initial A, which marks the Feast day of Saint Maurice and the Theban Legion (Sept. 22), was excised from a North Italian Antiphonary, another fragment of which appeared at auction in 1930 and has since not been traced.[2] Stylistically, its initial ornament and structure, figure types, landscape, and color scheme associated it with Lombard miniature painting of the mid and later fifteenth century, most of which shows heavy influence of the style of Belbello da Pavia and the Master of the Vitae Imperatorum. Specifically, the soldiers' faces (with their blond, wispy hair and half closed eyes) as well as the shaft ornament of the initials, the full leafy extenders, and the dark, craggy landscape with gold highlighting, bear comparison with miniatures by the so-called Master of the Franciscan Breviary.[3] A single anonymous miniature in the British Museum (cod. add. 38,897), however, is even more closely related.[4] The Augustinian monks flanking Saint Augustine in that miniature have round heads with high foreheads and low, rather prominent ears quite analogous to their counterparts in the Rosenwald fragment. Moreover, they show

the same meek expression. Finally, the background ornament of that fragment (crosses with dots), as well as the deep, undulating drapery of its Saint Augustine shows parallels in our miniature's sister initial.

Some of the qualities referred to are found in the profile portrait inserted in the border of a Virgil manuscript in a private Swiss collection, which carries the signature of a Lombard illuminator, Ambrogio da Marliano.[5] According to Professor Otto Pächt, both our cutting and its sister miniature are likely to be by him.[6]

1. Ball and Graupe, 1930, lot 13, illus.

2. See SISTER MINIATURE. Both fragments were sold out of the Czeczowitzka Collection, Vienna.

3. Levi D'Ancona, 1970, pp. 21ff. This illuminator is named from his only dated work (1446), a two volume Franciscan Breviary in Bologna (Biblioteca Universitaria, cod. 237). For the facial types and landscape compare the Ascension miniature formerly in the Wildenstein Collection (Levi D'Ancona, 1970, no. 2 pl. II). For the initial ornament compare the Ascension miniature in the Cini Collection, Venice (cod. 140) (Pietro Toesca, *La Collezione di Miniature di Ulrico Hoepli* (Milan 1930), no. XCVII, pl. XCI). The style of the Master of the Franciscan Breviary is generally more dynamic and expressive (in gesture, colors, drapery) than that of the Rosenwald miniature.

4. Mirella Levi D'Ancona, "Frate Nebridio," *Arte lombarda 8, no. 2* (1963), fig. 4. Although Professor Levi D'Ancona tentatively attributes this leaf to Don Nebridio, an Augustine monk who signed an initial E with a half figure of Saint Augustine in the Museo Civico, Bologna (cod. palagi 130), it shows significant differences from that one signed miniature.

5. E. Aeschlimann & P. d'Ancona, *Dictionnaire des Miniaturistes du moyen âge et de la renaissance*, 2nd ed. Milan, 1949, pl. LXXXII.

6. Professor Pächt characterizes our miniatures as "types of the Bonifazio Bembo repertoire curiously emaciated."

Fig. 22c. *Saint Ursula and her Maidens.*
Formerly: Vienna, Czeczowitzka Collection

Fig. 22a. 1:1

23

Initial G from a Choir Book
(Gradual)

*Saint Francis Receiving the
Stigmata*
Northern Italy (Ferrara),
c. 1460s, close to Cosimo Tura
B-13,524
184 x 174   (7 1/4 x 6 7/8)

Gothic minuscule script with four-line staff in red (49 mm)

CONDITION   (VG/E) Pigment surface very clear; gold tarnished and cracked but shows only minor rubbing; edges retouched in black (reverse: export stamp, Bologna)

PROVENANCE   E. Simon (up to 1929); J. Rosenthal, Munich (from 1929); E. Rosenthal, Berkeley; L. J. Rosenwald, Jenkintown (1946); National Gallery of Art (1946)

EXHIBITED   Baltimore, 1949, no. 180; illus.; Los Angeles, 1953–1954, no. 106, illus.; South Bend, 1972, no. 22

BIBLIOGRAPHY   P. Cassirer, *Edward Simon Collection* (1929), lot 2; Paul Wescher, "Buchminiaturen im Stil Cosimo Tura," *Berliner Museen, Berichte aus den Preussischen Kunstsammlungen* [*Beiblatt zum Jahrbuch der Preussischen Kunstsammlungen*] *51, no. 4* (1930), 79f., fig. 3; A. M. L. "Two Exhibitions in Munich," *The Burlington Magazine 59, no. 341* (Aug. 1935), 85; Paul Wescher, *Miniaturen—Handschriften und Einzelblätter—des Kupferstichkabinetts der Staatlichen Museen Berlin* (Leipzig 1931), p. 99; Emma Calabi, "I Corali miniati dell convento di S. Francesco a Brescia," *Critica d'arte 3, no. 2* (April 1938), 61

SISTER MINIATURES (?)[1]

1) Berlin, Kupferstichkabinett, cod. 4493: single initial N (389 x 289 mm; staff: 50 mm); Birth of the Virgin (*fig. 23c*)[2]

Fig. 23b. Recto

Fig. 23c. *The Birth of the Virgin.* Berlin, Staatliche Museen Preussischer Kulturbesitz, Kupferstich Kabinett, cod. 4493

Fig. 23a. 1:1

Fig. 23d. *John the Baptist*. Formerly: Paris, Wildenstein Collection

Fig. 23e. *Saint Francis*. Formerly: Paris, Wildenstein Collection

2) Formerly: Paris, Wildenstein Collection: single initial D (255 x 150 mm); John the Baptist (*fig. 23d*)[3]

3) Formerly: Paris, Wildenstein Collection: single initial I; Saint Francis (*fig. 23e*)[4]

4) New York, The Metropolitan Museum of Art, cod. 11.50.1: single initial A (444 x 304 mm); Assumption of the Virgin (*fig. 23f*)[5]

5) New York, The Metropolitan Museum of Art, cod. 11.50.2: single initial D (?) (368 x 305 mm); group of saints (*fig. 23g*)

6) New York, The Metropolitan Museum of Art, cod. 11.50.3: single initial G (346 x 311 mm); Assumption of the Virgin (*fig. 23h*)

7) New York, The Metropolitan Museum of Art, cod. 11.50.4: single initial G (?) (336 x 286 mm); Presentation in the Temple (*fig. 23i*)

RECTO (*fig. 23b*)   End of the offertory (([alle]luia); followed by the Communion rubric and the beginning of the Communion for the Feast of Saint Michael (Sept. 29): [Benedici] te o[mn]es ang[e]li.

VERSO (*fig. 23a*)   Beginning of the Feast of Saint Francis (Oct. 4): G[audeanmus omnes in Domino. . . .] (Let us all rejoice in the Lord. . . .)

Saint Francis, as well as the monk quietly reading beside a cell in the background, is dressed in a grayish-brown habit highlighted with fine lines of gold. Similar highlights accent the diaphanous shrubs and small trees that dot the light green landscape, and the greenish-blue river bed in which Francis kneels. The hybrid bird forming the initial G is predominantly rose with sections of light green and blue.

In August 1224 Saint Francis withdrew with several monks to the summit of La Verna, a mountain in the Apennines. He chose a cell apart from the others and only Brother Leo, his secretary and confessor, was allowed to come near him. In mid September, while in prayer upon the mountain, Francis saw a seraph descend from heaven bearing a Crucifix between his wings. The seraph spoke, explaining many hidden things, and the Crucifix imprinted upon the body of Francis, the wounds of Christ's Passion.

This initial, which marks the Feast of Saint Francis (Oct. 4), is one of several excised from an as yet untraced choir book.[6] Scholars have long associated the style of these cuttings with manuscripts produced in Ferrara during the artistic efflorescence generated by the Court of Borso d' Este (1450–1471),[7] comparing especially the sumptuous four-volume Bible now in Modena (Bilioteca Estense, cod. v. g. 12) illuminated by a team of artists between 1455 and 1461.[8] Specific attributions have been proposed to several of the painters employed at that court, including Cosimo Tura,[9] Guglielmo Giraldi,[10] and Jacopo Filippo Medici, called Argenta.[11]

Although it is difficult to isolate individual hands within the Ferrarese court style, the Rosenwald Saint Francis and its sister miniatures appear most closely related to works of Cosimo Tura. Specifically, the heavy, sculptural drapery should be compared with three small companion tondi now in Boston (Isabella Stewart Gardner Museum); Cambridge, Massachusetts (Fogg Art Museum no. 37); and New York (The Metropolitan Museum, Bache no. 14. 41. 49).[12] The Wildenstein John the Baptist is especially close to the tiny panel (210 x 120 mm) of Saint Maurelius (?) in the Museo Poldi-Pezzoli in Milan (no. 600),[13] while the facial types of the Berlin Nativity miniature are paralleled in panels in the National Gallery of Art, Washington (*Madonna and Child*, Samuel H. Kress Collection, no.

450),[14] and in the Accademia, Venice (*Madonna with Sleeping Child*, no. 628).[15]

In spite of the absence of signed manuscripts by Tura, there is reason to believe that he was a miniaturist, at least in his early career. This is suggested by a document of 1452 describing a commission received by Cosimo to paint miniatures on caskets: *Dorare cassette di muschio con miniature e rilievi.*[16] Further, some of Tura's small panels as well as the tiny Annunciation tondi in the upper corners of the National Gallery Madonna show him working on the scale of choir book initials.[17]

Closely related to the style of the Rosenwald miniature is a half-length figure heading a single leaf of a printed edition of the *Historia trojana* in Berlin (Kupferstichkabinett, cod. 3789),[18] and a miniature of the Virgin and Child in a Book of Hours in Basel (Öffentliche Kunstsammlung, cod. T.18), whose calendar points to Modena, Este, and Ferrara.[19]

Fig. 23f. *The Assumption of the Virgin.* New York, The Metropolitan Museum of Art, cod. 11.50.1

1. The precise relationship of these cuttings has yet to be determined. While some fragments bear Antiphonary texts (e.g. nos. 1, 4), others (including the Rosenwald miniature and nos. 2, 3, and 6) were apparently cut from a Gradual. Perhaps all were originally part of a companion set of choir books.

2. Paul Wescher, *Miniaturen—Handschriften und Einzelblätter—des Kupfer-stichkabinetts der Staatlichen Museen Berlin* (Leipzig 1931), p. 99, fig. 87. We would like to thank Dr. Peter Dreyer of the Kupferstichkabinett for making the staff measurement.

3. Amédée Boinet, *La Collection de miniatures de M. Edouard Kann* (Paris 1926), no. XXXIX, pl. XXXVII.

4. See note 3.

5. See Harvey Stahl, "Selected Manuscript Paintings from the Medieval Collection: Opens April 18, 1972," *The Metropolitan Museum of Art Bulletin 30, no. 5* (April/May 1972), 228, fig. 2. The association of the four New York fragments with the Rosenwald initial was made by Dr. Federico Zeri in 1966. We would like to thank Harvey Stahl for helpful discussions of these miniatures, and for measurements of the New York fragments. According to Mr. Stahl, another related fragment is in the Heseltine Collection, London.

6. See SISTER MINIATURES above.

7. Hermann J. Hermann, "Zur Geschichte der Miniaturmalerei am Hofe der Este in Ferrara," *Jahrbuch der Kunsthistorischen Sammlungen in Wien* (1909), pp. 117ff.

8. Hermann, 1909, pp. 119ff.; *Mostra storica nazionale della miniatura* (Rome: Palazzo di Venezia, 1953), no. 546, pl. LXXI; Mario Salmi, *La Miniatura Italiana* (Milan 1955), pls. LII–LV.

9. Paul Wescher: "Style of Tura" (Wescher, 1930, passim); Bernard Berenson: Tura himself (see Mario Salmi, *Cosmè Tura* [Milan 1957], p. 46).

10. Salmi, 1957, 46.

11. Calabi, 1938, 61.

12. Salmi, 1957, pls. XX–XXII.

13. Salmi, 1957, pl. XLIV.

14. Salmi, 1957, pl. I.

15. Salmi, 1957, pl. XII.

16. Salmi, 1957, 11; Piero Bianconi, *Tutta la pittura di Cosmè Tura* (Milan 1963), p. 14.

17. Eberhard Ruhmer, *Tura: Paintings and Drawings* (London 1958), pls. 32–33.

18. Wescher, 1931, 99f., fig. 88.

19. Konrad Escher, *Die Miniaturen in den Basler Bibliotheken, Museen und Archiven* (Basel 1917), no. 346, pl. LXXVII. The facial type, drapery, diaphanous trees, gemlike rocks, and clumps of grass are very close to the Rosenwald miniature.

Fig. 23h. *The Assumption of the Virgin.* New York, The Metropolitan Museum of Art, cod. 11.50.3

Fig. 23g. *Group of Saints*. New York, The Metropolitan
Museum of Art, cod. 11.50.2

Fig. 23i. *The Presentation in the Temple*. New York, The
Metropolitan Museum of Art, cod. 11.50.4

24

Leaf from a Choir Book (Gradual)

Saints Peter and Paul
Cremona, 1489, Ludovico de Gacis (scribe and illuminator)
Lessing J. Rosenwald Collection
570 x 407 (22 1/2 x 16)

Gothic minuscule script with four-line staff in red (27 mm); 7 lines, accompanied by staffs (364 x 268 mm)

CONDITION (E) Color and detail extremely fresh; only very minor rubbing; vellum and ink very well preserved

PROVENANCE Cremona; Belluno; Library of the Prince of Stolberg-Wernigerode, Wernigerode (cod. 40, up to the turn of the century); H. P. Kraus, New York; Mark Lansburgh, Colorado Springs; E. Rosenthal, Berkeley; L. J. Rosenwald, Jenkintown (1971)

BIBLIOGRAPHY Oscar Doering, "Die Miniaturen der Fürstlich Solbergischen Bibliothek zu Wernigerode," *Zeitschrift für Bucherfreunde 1* (1897–1898), 353f.; *Allgemeines Lexikon der bildenden Künstler 13* (Ulrich Thieme) (Leipzig 1920), p. 23; Erardo Aeschlimann, *Dictionnaire des miniaturistes* (Milan 1940), p. 72; H. P. Kraus, *Fifty Medieval and Renaissance Manuscripts* [Sale Catalogue no. 88, n.d.] (New York n.d.), no. 46; W. H. Bond and C. U. Faye, *Supplement to the Census of Medieval and Renaissance Manuscripts in the United States and Canada* (New York 1962), p. 25 (Lansburgh)

PARENT MANUSCRIPT Formerly: Colorado Springs, Mark Lansburgh Collection, cod. 5: 220 folios (570 x 408 mm); 13 historiated initials (*figs. 24c–24e*)[1]

RECTO Continuation of the Introit for the Vigil of Saints Peter and Paul (June 28): *et ducet te* [sic]; through the Psalm and Verse; followed by the rubric for the gradual and offertory; and the beginning of the Communion: *Si*[*mon*].

VERSO (*figs. 24a, 24b*) Communion for the Vigil of Saints Peter and Paul (June 28); followed by the rubric for the Feast of Saints Peter and Paul, and the beginning of the Introit: *Nunc scio vere . . . angelum sum*[*et*]. (Acts 12:11: Now I know in very deed . . .); original numeral XXXIII at upper left.

Saint Peter on the right with his symbolic keys, and Saint Paul on the left with his sword are dressed in complementary colors: the former in a green cloak with red lining, and the latter in a red cloak with green lining; Peter wears a magenta tunic, Paul a brown tunic. The sky is shaded from light blue at the horizon to dark blue near the top. The initial and its extenders are predominantly magenta and red, with occasional green accents.

This large single leaf, with its double portrait of Saints Peter and Paul marking the beginning of the mass for their feast day, was part of a choir book formerly in the Ducal Library at Wernigerode (cod. 40).[2] That codex carried the following scribal colophon:

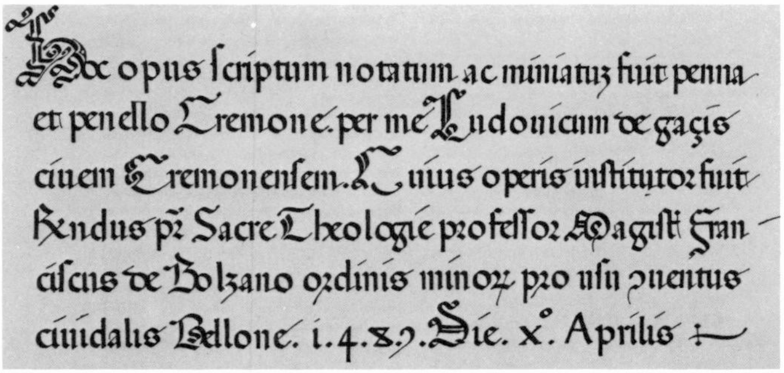
Hoc opus scriptum notatum ac miniatum fuit penna
et pencello Cremone per me Ludovicum de gacis
civem Cremonensem. Cuius operis institutor fuit
Reverendus pr Sacre Theologie professor Magister Franciscus de Bolzano ordinis minorum pro usu conventus
civitatis Bellone. 1.4.8.9. Die. x. Aprilis

Fig. 24c. *Scribal Colophon* dated April 10, 1489. Formerly: Colorado Springs, Mark Lansburgh Collection, cod. 5

mon iohan nis dili gis me pl'

his domi ne tu omnia no

sti tu scis do mi ne

In festo aplo
rum petri et 1
qui a a mo te. pauli introit.

Nc scio ue

re quia misit

dominus ange lum su um 7

Fig. 24a

Fig. 24b. Verso, detail, 1:1

This work was written, provided with musical notation, and illuminated with pen and brush by me, Lodovico de Gaçis, citizen of Cremona. The Patron of this work was the Reverend Father, professor of Holy Theology, Master Franciscus de Bolzano, of the minorite order, for the use of the convent in the city of Belluno. 1489. 10th day of April.[3]

Ludovico may well have been part of the Gadio family, several members of which were scribes and illuminators of choir books for various churches in Cremona from the 1440s to 1490s.[4] If that association is correct, Ludovico may have adapted the style of his (presumably) older brother Giovanni, a prominent master of the 1480s.[5] The two illuminators are easily distinguishable, for Ludovico stresses decoration, while Giovanni emphasizes complications in composition and figure style.

86

While some qualities exemplified by the Rosenwald leaf ultimately derive from the work of Mantegna and are to be found in a wide range of manuscripts connected to the schools of Mantua and Ferrara, the stylistic trend which it reflects appears in particular concentration in the work of Christoforo de Predis and a number of related illuminators active in Cremona during the last four decades of the fifteenth century.[6] Typical of the Cremonese manner are spindly decorative forms, crisply drawn figures, pyramidal berry ornaments, and calculated color harmonies.

1. See Kraus, n.d., no. 46, illus. pp. 102, 103, 105, 158. According to Mr. Lansburgh the codex has since been sold and dismembered.

2. See PROVENANCE and PARENT MANUSCRIPT. Professors Daneu Lattanzi and Mirella Levi D'Ancona plan a joint article that will consider the Rosenwald leaf and its sister miniatures.

3. *Hoc opus scriptum notatum ac miniatum fuit penna et penello Cremone. per me Ludovicum de gaçis civem Cremonensem. Cuius operis institutor fuit R[evere]ndus p[ate]r Sacre Theologie professor Magis[er] Franciscus de Bolzano ordinis Minor[is] pro usu [Con]ventus cividalis Bellone. 1. 4. 8. 9. Die. X°. Aprilis.* See Kraus, n.d., 102.

4. Felice Zanoni, "Lo 'Scriptorium' dei Gadio," *Annali della biblioteca governativa e libreria civica di Cremona 8, no. 2* (1955), xxivff.

   Perhaps "Gaci" is a corruption or misreading of "Gadi." See Felice Zamoni, "La Scuola miniaturistica Cremonese, 2. Scrittura e miniatura," *Annali della biblioteca governativa e libreria civica di Cremona 8, no. 2* (1955), xx.

5. His miniatures are to be found in Cremona, Cattedrale, cods. VIII and IX. See *Annali*, 1955, no. 1, figs. 35–37.

6. The principal choir books still in Cremona are catalogued and discussed by Alfredo Puerari, Felice Zanoni, Maria Luisa Ferrari, and Mina Gregori in *I Corali del Duomo di Cremona e la miniatura Cremonese nel quattrocento (Annali della biblioteca governativa e libreria civica di Cremona 8, nos. 1–3* [1955]). Note especially section one: Alfredo Puerari, "Orientamenti della pittura e della miniatura a Cremona nell'ultimo trentennio del quattrocento."

Fig. 24d. *The Virgin and Saint Joseph adoring the Christ Child.* Formerly: Colorado Springs, Mark Lansburgh Collection, cod. 5

Fig. 24e. *Group of Saints.* Formerly: Colorado Springs, Mark Lansburgh Collection, cod. 5

25

Leaf from a *Biblia Pauperum*

The Flight into Egypt (R);
*The Destruction of the
Egyptian Idols* (v)
North Italy, early 15th century
B-22,921
170 X 117   (6 11/16 x 4 5/8)

Gothic cursive script; three tier page division (bottom to top): two prophets framing a New Testament anti-type; two Old Testament types; two Old Testament texts framing two prophets

CONDITION   (F/G) Colors, ink faded and rubbed; vellum extensively stained in upper-left (gutter) corner, and along fore-edge; vellum crumbling in upper right (fore-edge) corner

PROVENANCE   E. Rosenthal, Berkeley; L. J. Rosenwald, Jenkintown (through L'Art Ancien, 1962); National Gallery of Art (1964)

EXHIBITED   Trenton, 1971, no. 30

SISTER MINIATURES   Boston, Public Library, cod. qMed. 164, eight single leaves (170 X 115 mm):[1]

1) *Recto:* The Annunciation; Temptation of Adam and Eve; Gideon's fleece; *Verso:* Nativity; Moses and the Burning Bush; Aaron's rod

2) *Recto:* Adoration of the Magi; Abner offers David the Kingdom; Queen of Sheba visits Solomon; *Verso:* Presentation in the Temple; the purification of a Jewish woman after the birth of her first-born; the infant Samuel brought before Eli [Rosenwald leaf]

3) *Recto:* Massacre of the Innocents; Saul kills priests who had aided David; the King's sons killed by Athaliah; *Verso:* Return from Egypt; David brought back to rule after Saul's death; Jacob returns to his own land

4) *Recto:* Baptism; Naaman cleanses himself in the Jordan; Judith bathing before going to kill Holofernes; *Verso:* Temptation of Jesus; Esau sells his birthright; Adam and Eve

5) *Recto:* Resurrection of Lazarus; Elijah and Elisha each bring back to life the son of a widow; *Verso:* the Transfiguration; three angels appear to Abraham; three Hebrews in the fiery furnace

6) *Recto:* Mary Magdalene at Christ's feet; David repents before Nathan; Moses and Aaron heal Miriam; *Verso:* Entry into Jerusalem; David with the head of Goliath; Elisha honored by prophet's children

7) *Recto:* Judas receives his payment; Joseph sold by his brothers; Absalom conspires against David; *Verso:* the Last Supper; Abraham and Melchizedek; the Fall of Manna

8) *Recto:* Jesus preaching to the Jews; Micah and Ahab; the King of Samaria sends men to kill Elisha; *Verso:* Christ in the Garden with prostrate soldiers; an angel smites the Assyrians; Elisha with the soldiers of the Syrian king

RECTO *(fig. 25a)*   In the bottom center is the Flight into Egypt (Matt. 2:13–14) with the Virgin and Child, and Joseph. In the tier above are two Old Testament parallels: (left) Rebecca (with Isaac) warns the fleeing Jacob against the wrath of Esau (Gen. 27:42–45); and (right) Michal helps David escape from the armed messengers of Saul gathered before her door, by lowering him from her window (I Sam. 19:11–12). The scenes are framed by four prophets with lettered scrolls: (from the upper left) Isaiah, David (crowned), Hosea, and Jeremiah.[2] The texts in the upper left and right are lections (biblical passages excerpted for liturgical purposes) relating to the Old Testament scenes. Their typological emphasis leads to variation from the biblical passages upon which they are based (Genesis 27 and I Samuel 19, respectively). Both begin with the word "*Legitur. . . .*"

The figures, drawn in brown ink on uncolored vellum, are filled with pale washes of yellow, lavender, brown, yellow orange, and blue.

VERSO *(fig. 25b)*   In the bottom center is the destruction of the Egyptian idols before the Virgin and Child (Pseudo-Matthew 23); above are: (left) Moses destroying the golden calf (Exod. 32:20) and (right) the destruction of the Philistine idol Dagon by the Ark of God (I Sam. 5:4). The lections are based on Exodus 31-35 (left) and I Samuel 5 (right), and the two identified prophets are Zechariah (left)

Fig. 25a. 1:1

and Hosea (right).[3]

The drawing of the verso is even more sketchy than that of the recto. Colored wash is limited to the olive gray of the Virgin's mantle.

This leaf, together with eight single leaves in the Boston Public Library, formed part of an unusually small *Biblia Pauperum* (Bible of the Poor).[4] Since the scenes of its recto and verso comprise the ninth and tenth sets of paired types and anti-types,[5] it originally would have been bound between the second and third Boston fragments.

The hypothetical parent codex of these nine leaves may be classed among those *Biblia Pauperum* in which the text is distinct from, rather than integrated into, the series of events represented. Compositionally, its arrangement is that catalogued by W. Schreiber as Type v[6] and by H. Cornell as Type IIa.[7] This arrangement places the New Testament scene below two flanking Old Testament scenes. It deviates, however, in transferring two of the four prophets from positions alongside the Christological scene to the top of the page.

To a certain extent the *Biblia Pauperum* represents a characteristically South German counterpart to the *Bible moralisée*, popular in France from the second half of the thirteenth century, and to the *Speculum humanae salvationis*, which had its greatest success in the Lowlands and the western part of the German Empire. Generally, the script and figure style of our leaf show similarities to a *Biblia Pauperum* in Salzburg (Benediktinerstift S. Peter, cod. 15),[8] datable to the very end of the fourteenth century. Further, its pen and ink technique bears comparison to a slightly later volume also in Salzburg (Benediktinerstift, S. Peter, cod. IX, 12).[9] On the other hand Adolfo Venturi, Pietro Toesca, and Otto Pächt have all suggested an origin in North Italy.[10] As such it would be a very early Italian imitation of the German *Biblia Pauperum*, and a predecessor of the Italian block book editions of that text. The scenes do not include landscape and architectural settings which begin to appear in the *Biblia Pauperum* around 1420. On the other hand the realistic treatment of faces and headgear suggests a date no earlier than c. 1400.

1. Edith A. Wright, "Two Copies of the *Biblia Pauperum*," *The Boston Public Library Quarterly 11, no. 1*. (Jan. 11959), 9ff.; Sotheby and Company, [Sale Catalogue: July 8, 1957] (London 1957), lot 67, illus.
2. Isaiah: *Ecce d[ominus] i[n]gr[e]dietur [in] egiptu[m]*; David: *Ecce elo[n]gaiu fugie[n]s*; Hosea: *Cade[n]t ad q[ue]re[n]dum dom[inum] . . . (?)*; Jeremiah: *Reliq[ui] dom[um] m[e]am dimisi h[ere]ditatem m[e]am.*
3. Zechariah: *In die illa disp[er]dam no[m]i[n]a ydolor[um]*; Hosea (?): *Actenuabit do[minus] o[mn]es deos d[e] te[rr]a.*
4. See SISTER MINIATURES. H. Cornell [*Biblia Pauperum* (Stockholm 1926)] catalogues only one *Biblia Pauperum* smaller than that represented by the Rosenwald fragment (p. 117, no. 65: Munich, Staatsbibliothek, cod. clm. 23499; 130 x 100mm); nos. 4 and 10 (pp. 73, 77) are only slightly larger.
5. Cornell, 1926, pp. 22f.
6. Wilhelm L. Schreiber, *Biblia Pauperum* (ed. Paul Heitz) (Strasbourg 1903), p. 30f.
7. Cornell, 1926, p. 6.
8. Cornell, 1926, no. 20, pls. 14–18.
9. Cornell, 1926, no. 17.
10. The opinion of Venturi and Toesca is quoted in the Sotheby sale catalogue cited in note 1: "Verona, Early 15th Century." Dr. Pächt, whom we would like to thank for helpful discussions of this leaf, has suggested Terra ferma (Treviso?).

Fig. 25b. Verso, 1:1

26

Leaf from a Sacramentary

Christ in Majesty (R)
Crucifixion (V)
Northern France (region of
Cambrai?), early 12th century
B-22,223
177 X 123   (6 15/16 X 4 13/16)

CONDITION   (F/G) Vellum extensively soiled, wrinkled, and rubbed (especially toward lower fore-edge); colors faded; vellum repaired toward lower fore-edge; numbered in upper center (recto: 74, verso: 76); severely trimmed

PROVENANCE   E. Rosenthal, Berkeley; L. J. Rosenwald, Jenkintown (1956); National Gallery of Art (1961)

EXHIBITED   *The Apocalypse* (College Park, Maryland: University of Maryland Art Gallery, 1973), no. 2, illus.

RECTO *(fig. 26a)*   Christ, enthroned within a mandorla, and the four Apocalyptic beasts that surround Him, are drawn in brown ink. A thick, deep red is used within the mandorla, as well as for the border, for haloes, and for the ornament on Christ's garments. All else is uncolored vellum, except for white areas within the mandorla, white highlighting on drapery, and a thin yellow wash in two haloes.

VERSO *(fig. 26b)*   Standard Crucifixion iconography is supplemented through a (faintly visible) hybrid serpent beneath the cross. The colors repeat those of the verso, with the cross and border background filled with alternating areas of thin yellow and deep red. Strangely, the fore-edge border ornament is nearly twice as wide as that of the gutter edge.

This single (trimmed) leaf probably once formed part of a Sacramentary (service book including all prayers recited by the celebrant at high mass), where the Crucifixion of its verso would have faced the *Te igitur* (Wherefore, O most merciful Father . . .) marking the beginning of the Canon. The highly stylized formula used for the articulation of the face, as well as aspects of its linear drapery style, and its rather full, undisciplined vegetal border ornament bear comparison with French Romanesque miniature painting from the region of Paris and farther north. The delineation of the Virgin's mouth (a flattened M over tangential, horizontal arcs), and the cascading lobes of hair of Christ and John (verso) find parallels in the figures of Saints Germain and Vincent in the frontispiece to a commentary of Origen in the Bibliothèque Nationale (cod. lat. 11615, fol. 2v), assigned to the early twelfth century and localized to the Parisian abbey of Saint-Germain-des-Près (of which the above saints are patrons).[1] Similarities may also be traced in a somewhat earlier (mid-eleventh century) Psalter-Hymnary (Paris, Bibliothèque Nationale, cod. lat. 11550), assigned on stylistic and liturgical grounds to Saint-Germain-des-Près.[2] Its illuminations show parallels for the expressive, pleated hems in the Rosenwald miniature, for the serpent beneath the cross, and the head type of Christ (fol. 6r, the Crucifixion), for the wide, leafy border of the verso (fol. 8r), and for the free application of gems and patterns to garments) fol. 7v. Specifically, the miniatures appear, however, closely related to a Lectionary in the Municipal Library of Cambrai (cod. 528 [487]), which was written by a monk, Rainer, for Saint-André-du-Cateau in the early twelfth century.[3]

1. *Manuscrits à peintures du* VIIe *au* XIIe *siècle*, (Paris: Bibliothèque Nationale, 1954), no. 250; Phillipe Lauer, *Les Enluminures romanes de la Bibliothèque Nationale* (Paris 1927), pl. LVIII.
2. Charles Niver, "Notes Upon an Eleventh-Century Psalter," *Speculum 3, no. 3* (July 1928), 398ff., pl. I, A, B; III, A; Lauer, 1927, pls. XXXII, LI–LII; Jean Porcher, *L'Enluminure Française* (Paris 1959), pl. III (color). That the Rosenwald miniature

Fig. 26a. 1:1

Fig. 26b. Verso, 1:1

style is substantially more advanced than that of the Psalter (convincingly assigned by Niver to the mid-eleventh century) is especially apparent in its gently swaying figure of Christ on the cross.
3. A. Durrieux, *Les Miniatures des manuscrits de la Bibliothèque de Cambray* (Cambrai, n.d.), pls. 4–5; and *Manuscrits*, 1954, no. 176.

27

Leaf from a Miscellany including Bede's *Explanatio Apocalypsis*, and Haymo of Auxerre's *in Apocalipsin*

Saint John dictating to Bede
Lambach, first half 12th century
B-17,715
352 x 235   (14 3/16 x 9 1/4)

38 lines (pin pricks), with a text block of 280 x 188 mm

CONDITION   (F) Vellum extensively soiled; many worm holes; larger holes and rust stains in upper and lower fore-edge corners; foliated *1* in upper right fore-edge; slash along lower gutter edge

PROVENANCE   Lambach, library of the Benedictine abbey; A. Mettler, Saint Gall (up to 1929); Baron von Thyssen, Schloss Rohoncz (by 1930); E. Rosenthal, Berkeley; L. J. Rosenwald, Jenkintown (1950); National Gallery of Art (1950)

EXHIBITED   *Sammlung Schloss Rohoncz* (Munich: Neue Pinakothek, 1930), no. 84, illus.; National Gallery, 1950, no. 2, illus.; Los Angeles, 1953–1954, no. 15, illus.; Trenton, 1971, no. 8

BIBLIOGRAPHY   Georg Swarzenski, *Die Salzburger Malerei* (2 vols.; Leipzig 1908, 1913; reprinted: Stuttgart 1969), p. 155n.; Mm.-Mensing et Fils (Frederik Muller et Cie.), *Catalogue d'une collection de manuscrits à miniatures des IXe–XVe siècles: Collection d'un amateur Suisse* [Sale Catalogue: Nov. 22, 1929] (Amsterdam 1929), lot 51, illus.; Kurt Holter, "Die romanische Buchmalerei in Oberösterreich," *Jahrbuch des Oberösterreichischen Musealvereines 101* (1956), 228; Kurt Holter, "Die Handschriften und Inkunabeln," *Die Kunstdenkmäler des Gerichtsbezirkes Lambach* (Österreichische Kunsttopographie 34, no. 2), ed. Erwin Hainisch (1959), 214, fig. 226

PARENT MANUSCRIPT   Lambach, Stiftsbibliothek, cod. VI: 2 columns of 38 lines; retains ornamental initials and an author portrait of Bede (fol. 37v); the Rosenwald leaf was folio 1 (*figs. 27d, 27e*)[1]

RECTO *(fig. 27b):*   Sketch for initial A with two beasts, perhaps a copy of that marking the beginning of Bede's *Epistola ad Eusebium* which precedes his commentary in the parent manuscript:[2] *Apocalypsis sancti Joannis . . .* ; brown-black ink with thin washes of green and yellow.

VERSO *(figs. 27a, 27c):*   John (*Ioh[anne]s*), seated on a pillowlike representation of the island of Patmos, dictates to the Venerable Bede (inscription partially erased) who sits at the desk of a scribe with a feather quill, knife, and ink horn. The Dove of the Holy Spirit descends from an architectural superstructure, imparting divine inspiration to John. This drawing, like that of the recto, is colored in various shades of green and pale yellow. The four-line frame along the sides and bottom is red.

This single leaf was formerly folio 1 of a manuscript in the library of the Benedictine cloister at Lambach (upper Austria).[3] The double portrait of its verso, John dictating to Bede, originally served as frontispiece to Bede's *Commentary on the Apocalypse*.[4] The initial A of its recto, as well as the two hybrid beasts that accompany it, are executed in a later style different from that of the portraits (compare the "bird" with the Holy Dove; or the bird's outstretched hand with the hands of Bede). Since it also is not equal to the initials of the Lambach codex itself,[5] and furthermore is not linked to any text passage, it is reasonable to suppose that this initial was added as a sketch by another illuminator, sometime after the completion of the codex, on the unused opening page. That same hand clumsily added green and yellow washes to areas of the double portrait and began a vegetal design within the left framing column.[6]

The decoration of this leaf and the parent codex from which it was excised has been associated with a group of manuscripts written and illuminated in Lambach just prior to the mid-twelfth century

Fig. 27a

flowering of its scriptorium. (Thus not far removed from the foundation of the cloister by Adalbero of Würzburg.) Especially closely related are the colored initials in two manuscripts still in Lambach: codices CXXXI and XLII.[7] Also part of the group are several manuscripts that are no longer at the monastery: Vienna, Nationalbibliothek, cods. 3599 and 3610 (formerly, Lambach cods. LXVII and CXIII) which include ornamental initials;[8] and an Apocalypse with a closely related portrait of John, sold through Sotheby in 1929.[9]

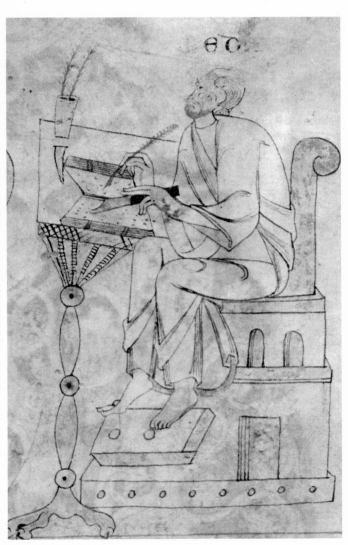

Fig. 27c. Recto, detail, 1:1

Fig. 27e. *Bede* (fol. 37v) Lambach, Stiftsbibliothek, cod. VI (detail)

1. The opening text leaf of the parent manuscript is missing. In its present condition the text begins: *te[m]poris, v[e]l reru[m]* . . . , or about sixty percent into the *Epistola*. The opening leaf would have had ample room for a large decorative initial A. (For the text of Bede's letter see note 4.)

2. Holter, 1959, 214, figs. 223, 227.

3. See PARENT MANUSCRIPT. Its upper right fore-edge is foliated *1*. A considerable number of manuscripts and single leaves left the smaller Austrian monastic libraries in the 1920s (especially Seittenstetten [see cat. 41], Admont, and Lambach).

4. J.-P. Migne, *Patrologiae cursus completus . . . series Latina prior, vol. 93* (Paris 1862), coll. 129ff.

5. Compare that marking the beginning of the Apocalypse text proper on folio 2v (Holter, 1959, fig. 223). No precise counterpart seems to exist for the thorny vegetal forms or for the technique of defining the leaf's outer surface "in silhouette," among early twelfth-century Lambach initials.

6. The washes are not logically correlated to John's garments; the area between his left elbow and torso has incongruously been filled in with green. The portrait of Bede on folio 37v of codex VI is uncolored.

7. Holter, 1959, p. 214, figs. 224–225.

8. Holter, 1959, p. 214n.

9. Holter, 1959, p. 214n., fig. 228. Compare especially the architectural frame.

Fig. 27d. *Initial A* (fol. 2v). Lambach, Stiftsbibliothek, cod. VI (detail)

Fig. 27b. Recto

28

Leaf from a Bible or Gospel
Book   (?)

*Nine Apostles preparing for the
Washing of the Feet (?) (R)
Crucifixion (v)*
Upper Catalonia or Andorra(?)
c. 1180–1200
B-22,018
250 x 174   (9 7/8 x 6 7/8)

CONDITION   (F/G) Vellum stained and wrinkled; pigment extensively flaked and rubbed; four slits along gutter edge (where removed from binding); colors of verso (grain side) better preserved; R. Forrer stamp (R)—Lugt suppl. 941a

PROVENANCE   R. Forrer, Strasbourg; E. Rosenthal, Berkeley; L. J. Rosenwald, Jenkintown (1955); National Gallery of Art (1958)

EXHIBITED   Trenton, 1971, no. 7

RECTO *(fig. 28a)*   Since these nine undifferentiated male figures are all haloed and in several cases appear to be drawing their garments up away from bare legs and feet, the miniature may represent the right half of a double page composition of the Washing of the Feet.[1] The figures, rendered in thick lines of dark brown ink, wear garments colored with dull washes of yellow, green, and dark reddish brown. The background of the upper field is gray; that of the lower, yellow. The braided ornament along the right has been left uncolored.

VERSO *(fig. 28b)*   While the Virgin and Saint John wear garments colored with thin washes like those of the recto (for both figures, gray over yellow), the remaining colors of the verso are much denser and brighter. The cross is deep green, outlined in thick, deep red, and the background bright yellow. The personifications of the sun (carrying a symbolic torch) and moon are dressed in deep red garments.

Although the color scheme and expressive primitivism of this leaf suggest a Spanish Romanesque origin, its provincial figure style makes a precise localization difficult. As François Bucher has pointed out,[2] the large, swaying figure of Christ with drooping head and closed eyes clearly reflects the influence of Byzantine models, and thus indicates a dating in the last decades of the twelfth century.[3] Further, Professor Bucher has suggested a localization to northern Catalonia or Andorra, citing the frontal of *Espinelvas* (c. 1187) in the Museo Episcopal of Vich as a general stylistic parallel.[4] Comparisons for the simple linear style of the Rosenwald miniatures, as well as for the decorative spiral at Christ's navel, may be found in an earlier twelfth-century panel also assigned to Catalonia: the frontal of *San Saturnino de Tabérnoles* (Barcelona, Museo de Arte de Cataluña).[5] Finally, the general proportions (if not the level of execution) of the Rosenwald Virgin are close to those of the Virgin in the frontispiece to a document from the monastery of San Martin del Canigó, dated 1195.[6]

1. The discontinuity at the line crossing the ankles of the figures suggests the optical distortion resulting from immersion in water. Christ washing the feet of the first three Apostles would have been on the facing page.
2. We would like to thank Professor Bucher for a very informative letter of April 29, 1974. For his overview of twelfth-century Spanish painting, see François Bucher, *The Pamplona Bibles* (New Haven 1970), pp. 45ff.
3. For a "pre-Byzantine" Crucifixion miniature in a North Catalonian Gospel book at Vich (Museo Episcopal, cod. 15), see J. Domínguez Bordona, "Miniatura: La Miniatura del período románico en Cataluña," *Ars Hispaniae 18* (1962), 94, fig. 13.
4. Walter Cook, "Pintura sobre tabla: Cataluña y Rosellón," *Ars Hispaniae 6* (1950), 215, figs. 187–188.
5. Cook, 1950, p. 194, fig. 166.
6. Bordona, 1962, p. 95, fig. 114. For a twelfth-century Gospel book from the same region (Cuixá) showing full-page narrative miniatures divided horizontally at midpoint (like the Rosenwald recto miniature), see Bordona, 1962, 93, fig. 100. (Perpignan, Biblioteca Municipal, cod. 1).

Fig. 28a. 1:1

Fig. 28b. Verso, 1:1

29

Bisected Leaf from a Sacramentary

Saints Cyprian, Vitus, Stephan, and Cornelius

Corvey (?), third quarter 12th century

B-22,909 (A); B-22,908 (B)

A 103 X 135   (4 1/16 X 5 5/16)

B 109 X 142   (4 5/16 X 5 5/8)

Primitive Gothic minuscule script; 1 column of 17 lines (184 x 120 mm)

CONDITION   (G) Vellum gray, stained, and rubbed; numerous worm holes; holes and slits along borders (A: top; B: bottom); glue stains; ink and colors faded (A: vellum is fresher, whiter)

PROVENANCE   Stitch-holes, creases, stains, and traces of glue indicate that these cuttings were at one time glued to the inside covers of a small volume (Book of Hours?), and were sewn to the first gathering in order to strengthen the binding;[1] Benedictine abbey of Zwiefalten; Herts County Museum, Hertfordshire, England; E. Rosenthal, Berkeley; L. J. Rosenwald, Jenkintown (1962 through L'Art Ancien); National Gallery of Art (1964)

EXHIBITED   Trenton, 1971, no. 4

A, RECTO *(fig. 29a)*   Beginning of the preface to the mass: *V[ere] D[ignum et justum est, ae]quum. . . .* B Direct continuation of the preface, up to: *. . . S[an]c[tu]s D[omi]n[u]s D[eu]s.*

The initials are drawn in bright red ink against a field of dark gray and pale yellow (left), and dark green and pale yellow (right). The interstices of the spiraling acanthus (which is uncolored vellum) are filled in random alterations of the same pigments.

A, VERSO *(fig. 29b)*   Direct continuation of the Preface from the recto (*Et id[e]o cu[m] . . .*), up to the end of the Sanctus. B The saints (left to right) are: Cyprian (*Cyprianus*), Vitus (*Vit[us]*), Stephan (*Stephan*), and Cornelius (*Corn[e]lius*). They are drawn in shades of brown, red, dark green, and blue against a field of uncolored vellum; their red haloes are filled with a thin yellow wash. Saints Cyprian (bishop of Carthage), Stephan ("deacon" and protomartyr), and Cornelius (third-century pope) are dressed in comparable ecclesiastical garments: a chasuble over a dalmatic, which covers a tunic. Cyprian wears an inscribed *Rationale* (counterpart to the pallium of the other two), an episcopal humeral not uncommonly used by German bishops during the Middle Ages.[2] While the vestments of Cyprian and Cornelius are appropriate to their rank (the latter wears a papal crown), Stephan would customarily wear the dalmatic of a deacon.[3]

The four saints of this bisected leaf would originally have preceded the *Te igitur* (Most merciful Father, we humbly pray and implore you . . .) marking the beginning of the Canon of the mass in a Sacramentary. The portrayal of Saints Cornelius and Cyprian reflects their inclusion among the Common Communicantes recited in the Canon soon after the *Te igitur*.[4] The inclusion of Vitus (rarely depicted in medieval art)[5] and Stephan, on the other hand, probably reflects the local hagiographic tradition of the monastery at Corvey. Both were patron saints of that foundation; the relics of Vitus had been deposited there since the ninth century.[6]

The Rosenwald leaf is stylistically related to the frontispiece miniature of a Cicero manuscript produced in Corvey in the 1150s (Tübingen, Stiftung Preuss. Kulturbesitz, Depot der Berlin Staatsbibliothek, cod. lat. fol. 252).[7] The upper half of that miniature (a dedication scene) includes closely comparable standing frontal portraits of Saints Vitus and Stephan, rendered in brown ink on uncolored vellum. Especially similar are the formulas used for the articulation of the eyes, nose, and mouth; the tight curls framing the face; and the sketchy treatment of the drapery. Moreover, that codex is ornamented with comparable red silhouette initials.[8] Additional

parallels may be cited among manuscripts produced around mid-century in Corvey or neighboring Helmarshausen for the script,[9] *VD* initials,[10] and the attention to ecclesiastical garments[11] evident in the Rosenwald fragments.

The Cicero manuscript was a product of the artistic and cultural revival fostered at the Corvey monastery by Wibald of Stavelot, abbot from 1147 until his death in 1158.[12] The strong Mosan quality of both the Cicero and Rosenwald miniatures may be explained through the intermediary role played by Wibald, who was also abbot of Stavelot from 1130 to 1158.[13]

1. I owe these observations to Mr. Christopher Clarkson.

2. *The Catholic Encyclopedia*, eds. Charles G. Hebermann et al., (New York 1913), vol. 12, pp. 651f. (Joseph Braun)

3. As he does in the closely related Cicero frontispiece cited in note 7.

4. ". . . Clement, Sixtus, Cornelius, Cyprian, Lawrence. . . . " In addition they share the same feast day (Sept. 16).

5. See Joseph Braun, *Tracht und Attribute der Heiligen in der Deutschen Kunst* (Stuttgart 1943), pp. 727ff.

6. *Kunst und Kultur im Weserraum 800–1600* (Corvey 1966), vol. 2, p. 499.

7. Corvey, 1966, no. 187, fig. 182. See also Albert Boeckler, "Corveyer Buchmalerei unter Einwirkung Wibalds von Stablo," *Westfälische Studien: Alois Bömer zum 60. Geburtstag Gewidmet* (Leipzig 1928), pp. 133f., fig. 1.

8. Corvey, 1966, no. 187.

9. Compare Kassel, Murhardsche Bibliothek der Stadt Kassel und Landes-bibliothek, cod. theol. 2° 58 (Corvey, 1966, no. 189, fig. 193a; "Helmarshausen c. 1160–1170").

10. Compare Uppsala, University Library, cod. c 83, fol. 18r (Boeckler, 1928, fig. 7).

11. Compare Uppsala, University Library, cod. c 83 (Corvey, 1966, no. 182, fig. 180; "Helmarshausen c. 1140"), and Münster, Staatsarchiv, cod. I 133 (Corvey, 1966, no. 188; "Helmarshausen c. 1158").

12. Boeckler, 1928, pp. 133ff.

13. Boeckler, 1928, pp. 134ff. For the discussion of a stylistically related (though earlier) Mosan Sacramentary (Brussels, Bibliothèque Royale, cod. 2034–2035) and its ties via Wibald to Helmarshausen see *Rhin-Meuse: Art et Civilisation 800–1400* (Cologne: Kunsthalle, and Brussels: Musées Royaux d'Art et d'Histoire, 1972), no. J18, illus.

quuoq̃ et salutare · Nos tibi semp
æubiq̃; grãs agere · dñe ĩce pater
ompē ẽtne dš · p xpm dñm nrm · P er
g̃ue maiestate tuã laudant angeli ·
adorant dominationes · tremunt potesta
tes · Celi celoxq̃; uirtutes · ac beata sera
phyn soc̃ia exultatione concelebrant ·
Cũ quib; et nras uoces ut admitti iu
beas depc̃ãm · supplici confessione
dicentes · Sc̃s · Sc̃s · Sc̃s · dñs dš

E tuo cu angelis et archangelis cum
thronis & dominationib;: cumq; o
milicia celestis exercitus ymnu g
tue canimus·sine fine dicentes
S cs·s cs·s cs·dns ds sab roth·p le
sunt celi et terra gla tui osanna
excelsis· enedictus qui uenit in
nine dni osanna in excelsis·

Fig. 29b. Verso; A, B, 1:1

30

Leaf from a Sacramentary

Crucifixion
North German or Danish (?),
late 12th century
B-14,843
184 x 127 (7 1/4 x 5)

Late Romanesque minuscule script; 1 column of 16 lines (perhaps originally 18) (c. 120 mm wide)

CONDITION   (F/G) Vellum stained and soiled; miniature extensively flaked and rubbed; rust-stained hole along right (recto) edge; foliated 2 in upper right; cross inscription in a later hand; 17 words (two lines?) of text apparently trimmed from bottom

PROVENANCE   E. Rosenthal, Berkeley; L. J. Rosenwald, Jenkintown (1947); National Gallery of Art (1948)

EXHIBITED   National Gallery, 1950, no. 5, illus.; Trenton, 1971, no. 9 illus.; South Bend, 1972, no. 1, illus.

RECTO *(fig. 30a)*   Last third of the Common Preface, beginning: [*Vir*]*tutes, ac beata* . . . ; followed by the Sanctus (abbreviated) up to: . . . *p*[*leni*] *s*[*unt*]. . . .

Christ, represented with open eyes (partially flaked), is suspended before a light green cross. His loin cloth is blue as are the mantles of the Virgin and John; their tunics are light brown. The panels of the background are brown and gold, and are enclosed by a blue frame.

VERSO   Beginning of the Canon of the mass: *Te igitur* . . . (to) . . . *cognita est, et nota.*

This (trimmed) single leaf was apparently folio 2 of a Sacramentary, the liturgical text comprising all the prayers recited by the celebrant at high mass: Collect, Secret, Postcommunion, and the Canon. Its Crucifixion miniature interrupts the final passage of the Common Preface to the mass (Heaven and earth are full of Your glory . . .), and thus immediately precedes the Canon which begins on the verso: Most merciful Father, we humbly pray and implore you. . . .

Because of its provincial figure style, the dating and localization of this fragment is especially difficult. While its blue, purple-brown, and gold tonality reflect early Gothic developments from around 1200, its composition, drawing, and drapery style recall North German illumination of several decades earlier.[1] For example, the general proportions, facial types, and poses of John and the Virgin, as well as the rectangular division of the background, and the fall and articulation of the drapery (modeling in white), are paralleled in the Crucifixion miniature of the *Psalter of Henry the Lion* (London, British Museum, cod. Lansdowne 381), written and illuminated at Helmarshausen around 1167.[2] The alternately colored rectangles which serve as background decoration appear commonly in twelfth-century miniature painting of North Germany, Denmark, and the Mosan region. Ultimately such motifs recall the stylistic conventions of metalwork.[3]

1. The unusual feature of the widening terminations of the cross is paralleled in a thirty-miniature cycle of the life of Christ in the Pierpont Morgan Library (cod. M44), for which a localization to Northeast France, c. 1200, has recently been proposed. See *The Year 1200: A Centennial Exhibition at The Metropolitan Museum of Art, I* (New York: The Metropolitan Museum of Art, 1970), no. 242, illus., p. 243.
2. *Kunst und Kultur im Weserraum 800–1600* (Corvey 1966), no. 191, illus. 185. Compare also the poses and gestures of both John and the Virgin in a mid-century Crucifixion miniature in a Helmarshausen Psalter in Baltimore (Walters Art Gallery, cod. w10) [Baltimore, 1949, no. 24, pl. xxi]. In the London and Baltimore miniatures the figure of Christ on the cross is much smaller and less rhythmically disposed than in the Rosenwald leaf. For the discussion of a highly refined Lower Saxon (Hildesheim, 1150s?) Canon page Crucifixion miniature recently acquired by the Museum of Fine Arts, Houston (no. 71.8), see

Fig. 30a. 1:1

J. L. Schrader, "The Canon Page from a Lost Sacramentary and its Significance to Romanesque Lower Saxon Style," *Bulletin, The Museum of Fine Arts, Houston (n.s.) 11, no. 8* (Dec. 1971), 142ff.
3. The attribution of the miniature to a Scandinavian workshop cannot be supported by direct parallels among the few illuminated manuscripts known to have been produced in Denmark or Sweden about this time. The primitivism of the design recalls, however, a group of enamelled reliquaries, no doubt of Danish origin, datable to the earlier half of the twelfth century, on which see P. Nörlund, "An Early Group of Enamelled Reliquaries," *Acta archaelogica*, iv, 1933, pp. 1-32.

31

Initial P from a Bible

The Judge Judah (?)
Lower Saxony (Halberstadt?),
1210–1220
B-18,757
229 x 144   (9 1/16 x 5 11/16)

Late Romanesque minuscule script; 1 (of 2) column of 24 lines (incomplete); column c. 111 mm wide

CONDITION   (G) Vellum soiled and rubbed; some script lost; several areas of pigment scraped and rubbed; facial detail precise (verso: R. Forrer stamp—Lugt suppl. 941a)

PROVENANCE   Halberstadt; R. Forrer, Strasbourg; E. Rosenthal, Berkeley; L. J. Rosenwald, Jenkintown (1950); National Gallery of Art (1950)

EXHIBITED   National Gallery, 1950, no. 4, illus.; Los Angeles, 1953–1954, no. 21, illus.; Trenton, 1971, no. 10, illus.; South Bend, 1972, no. 2, illus.

BIBLIOGRAPHY   Tilmann Buddensieg in *Kunstchronik 11, no. 9* (Sept. 1958), 242f.

PARENT MANUSCRIPT   Halberstadt, Dommuseum, cod. 3: 254 folios (470 x 330 mm); 2 columns (*figs. 31b, 31c*)[1]

RECTO (*fig. 31a*)   Judg. 1:1—Judg. 1:5 (*. . . in Besech [et]*). (Now after the death of Joshua it came to pass. . . .)

   This figure, perhaps Judah who is called by the Lord in verse 2 (Judges) to defend the Israelites against the Canaanites, wears a dark brown mantle over a light red tunic, modeled with white. The yellow and red initial he supports is set against a pale yellow background, framed by dark blue and green, and is filled with an acanthus leaf of red, green, blue, and yellow. The opening capital letters of verse one are alternately red and blue.

VERSO   Judg. 1:10—Judg. 1:16 (*. . . et habitaver[un]t*).

This miniature was once part of a large, two-column Bible in Halberstadt (Dommuseum, cod. 3),[2] whose decorative program includes anthropomorphic and zoomorphic initials marking the beginnings of the respective Books. The miniatures of this manuscript are central members of a small stylistic group of early thirteenth-century illuminations produced in Lower Saxony and associated through characteristic "Byzantinizing" facial types, fluid drapery, lively color combinations, and dragon-filled acanthus ornament.[3] Most closely related are the portraits of Matthew and Mark (fols. 13v and 38r) in a Gospel book fragment in the Pierpont Morgan Library (cod. M565),[4] and the "soft style" miniatures (ten figurative initials and two full-page compositions) in the Brandenburg Evangeliary (Brandenburg, Domarchiv).[5]

   Beyond the fact that two of these manuscripts are still to be found in Saxony, there is ample evidence linking the group with that North German region. The Morgan Library Gospels, for example, carry a fourteenth-century notice (fol. 1r) designating the monastic foundation at Heiningen, near Goslar.[6] Further, the other half of the New York Gospels (London, British Museum, cod. add. 27, 926),[7] contains Evangelist portraits in an earlier style closely related to another Bible in Halberstadt (Dommuseum, cod. 1), which carries a notice naming the Hamersleben monastery within the diocese of Halberstadt.[8] The fluid drapery of the Morgan miniatures bears comparison with the Apostles of the choir stalls in the Liebfrauenkirche in Halberstadt (c. 1200),[9] and the medallions of its cover, although dating from later in the century, find their closest counterparts in Lower Saxony.[10] Finally, Edith Rothe has shown that the Brandenburg Evangeliary has ties both to the choral foundation of the

Fig. 31b. *God the Father* (fol. 6v). Halberstadt, Dommuseum, cod. 3 (detail)

Brandenburg Cathedral and, through several particular lections, to a Magdeburg liturgical tradition.[11]

While the miniatures in the Halberstadt, Brandenburg, and New York codices were probably all produced within a short span of years in the early thirteenth century, the decoration of the Halberstadt Bible (with the Rosenwald fragment) is stylistically the most advanced. Specifically, it shows aspects of the angular, expressive drapery that appears in Saxony in the second decade of the century with the Landgraf Psalter (Stuttgart, Landesbibliotek, cod. H.B.II. fol. 24),[12] and the Crucifixion miniature of the *Libellus de consecratione*

POST
MOR
TEM
IOSVE

consuluerunt filij isr̃ł do
minū dicentes. Q̃s ascen
det ante nos contra chana
neū & erit dux belli. Dixit
q̃; dñs. Judas ascendet.
ecce tradidi terrā in manu
ei. Et ait iudas symeoni
fr̃i suo. Ascende mecū insorte mea.
& pugna contra chananeū. ut &
ego pgam tecum in sorte tua. Et a
biyt cū eo symeon. Ascendit q̃; iudas.
& tradidit dñs chananeū ac phere
zeū in manus eoʒ & pcusserunt
in besech decem milia uiroʒ. Jnue
nerunt q̃; adoni besech in besech &

Fig. 31a. 1:1

crismatis (formerly: Magdeburg, Domgymnasium, cod. 152),
commissioned in 1214 by Henry of Jerico, an assistant to Archbishop
Albert II of Magdeburg.¹³ The miniatures in the Morgan and
Brandenburg manuscripts, on the other hand, show a softer drapery
style bearing remnants of twelfth-century linear fold patterns.¹⁴

1. Alfred Stange, "Beiträge zur Sächsischen Buchmalerei des 13. Jahrhunderts,"
Münchner Jahrbuch der Bildenden Kunst (n.f.) 6 (1929), 318ff., fig. 11; and
Edith Rothe, *Buchmalerei aus zwölf Jahrhunderten* (Berlin 1966), p. 195, pl. 35.
2. See note 1. Judging from the text gap between obverse and reverse, this
initial originally occupied the right hand column of a recto page.
3. See Buddensieg, 1958, 242 f.; and Stange, 1929, 314ff.
4. Meta Harrsen, *Central European Manuscripts in the Pierpont Morgan
Library* (New York: The Pierpont Morgan Library, 1958), no. 26, pls. 45–46.
5. Josef Gülden, Edith Rothe, and Bernhard Opfermann, *Brandenburger
Evangelistar* (Düsseldorf 1962), passim. The figurative initials (with Gülden
plate numbers) are: 5v (pl. 6); 13r (pl. 13); 57r (pl. 37); 89v (pl. 44); 90v
(pl. 60); 94r (pl. 49); 96r (pl. 53); 97r (pl. 57); 98v (pl. 58); 100r (pl. 59). The
full page miniatures are: 95r (pl. 51); 97v (pl. 54).
6. *Liber b[ea]tissimor[um] ap[os]t[o]lor[um] Petri et Pauli i[n] henige[n]
ordi[ni]s canonicar[um] regulariu[m]*. See Buddensieg, 1958, 243.
7. *Catalogue of Additions to the Manuscripts in the British Museum: 1854–1875*,
(London 1877, reprint 1967), vol. 2, p. 387. See: Victor Habicht, *Niedersächsische
Kunst in England* (Hanover 1930), pp. 12ff. figs. 12–13.
8. Rothe, 1966, pl. 27. See also Habicht, 1930, 12; and Arthur Haseloff, "Die
Mittelalterliche Kunst," *Meisterwerke der Kunst aus Sachsen und Thüringen*,
ed. Oscar Doering (Magdeburg, 1905), pp. 93ff.
9. Oscar Doering, *Die Kirchen von Halberstadt* (Cologne/Vienna 1927),
figs. 23–24.
10. Georg Swarzenski, "Aus dem Kunstkreis Heinrichs des Löwen," *Städel-
Jahrbuch 7–8* (1932), 301ff.; and Erich Meyer, "Spätromanische Abendmahlskelche
in Norddeutschland," *Jahrbuch der Preuszischen Kunstsammlungen 53* (1932), 167ff.
11. Gülden, Rothe, Opfermann, 1962, pp. 61ff.
12. Karl Löffler, *Der Landgrafenpsalter* (Leipzig 1925), passim.
13. See Haseloff, 1905, pl. 117 (3).
14. Compare the Brandenburg John initial (fol. 5v) with the Halberstadt initial
of God the Father (fol. 6v). Romanesque nested-v folds are to be found for
example in the right sleeve of the Morgan Library Saint Matthew. Thanks are
due to Dr. John Plummer for helpful discussions of this group of miniatures.

Fig. 31c. *Initial H* (fol. 33v). Halberstadt, Dommuseum,
cod. 3 (detail)

32

Leaf from a Psalter

Crucifixion (R) The Three Women at the Tomb (V)
South Germany (Augsburg), after 1235
B-14,049
184 x 127   (7 1/4 x 5 1/16)

CONDITION   (VG/E) Colors and facial detail very fresh and precise; only very minor flaking of gold; silver heavily tarnished with minor flaking; diagonal crease across upper recto; trimmed.

PROVENANCE   V. Goldschmidt, Heidelberg (mid-1930s); said to have entered a Viennese collection; E. Rosenthal, Berkeley; L. J. Rosenwald, Jenkintown (1946); National Gallery of Art (1947)

EXHIBITED   Baltimore, 1949, no. 34; Los Angeles, 1953–1954, no. 22, illus.; Trenton, 1971, no. 15; South Bend, 1972, no. 4, illus.

BIBLIOGRAPHY   Hanns Swarzenski, *Die Lateinischen illuminierten Handschriften des XIII. Jahrhunderts in Ländern an Rhein, Main und Donau* (Berlin 1936), p. 58, no. 58, figs. 735-736; A. H. van der Beek-Scheffer, "Nog twee miniaturen vor het Augsburgse psalter in Praag," *Miscellanea I. Q. van Regteren Altena, 16/v/1969* (Amsterdam 1969), pp. 10ff., fig. 5

PARENT MANUSCRIPT   Prague, University Library, cod. XIV E 3:[1] 188 folios (273 x 180 mm); 1 column of 17 lines; Rosenwald miniature preceded Psalm 1

SISTER MINIATURES
1) Nuremberg, Germanisches Nationalmuseum, cod. MM26: single leaf (c. 185 x 125 mm); Annunciation (r) *(fig. 32c)*, Nativity (v) *(fig. 32d)*[2]
2) Nuremberg, Landesgewerbemuseum, cod. v. 24 nr. 1925–1926: single leaf (c. 185 x 125 mm); Adoration of the Magi (r) *(fig. 32e)*; Presentation in the Temple (v) *(fig. 32f)*[3]
3) Formerly: Robert Horst Collection: single leaf; Entry into Jerusalem (r), Last Supper (v)[4]
4) Nuremberg, Germanisches Nationalmuseum, cod. MM27: single leaf (c. 185 x 125 mm); Betrayal (r) *(fig. 32g)*, Christ Carrying the Cross (v) *(fig. 32h)*[5]
5) Lucerne, Kofler-Truniger Collection: single leaf (178 x 122 mm); Ascension (r) *(fig. 32i)*; *Majestas Domini* (v) *(fig. 32j)*[6]

RECTO *(fig. 32a)*   The Virgin wears a light burgundy mantle over a green tunic, which in turn covers a light blue undergarment; her veil is green. John's mantle is red, his tunic a greenish brown, and his undergarment light blue. The sun (upper left) is bright red, while the moon is modeled in shades of blue, as are Christ's loincloth and all haloes. Christ's beige flesh tones and the dark brown cross stand out against the highly burnished gold background.

VERSO *(fig. 32b)*   (Mark 18: 1-7) The angel, in a dark blue mantle and a light red tunic, sits atop a green marble sarcophagus, over whose forward edge is draped Christ's shroud. The angel's flesh tones are deep pink, in clear contrast with the pale beige of the other figures. The approaching holy women are dressed in brightly colored garments of red, green, burgundy, and blue; the Virgin carries a censer and Mary Magdalene a spice jar. Below, the soldiers wear (tarnished) silver armor and tunics of blue, red, and light burgundy. The patterned border is alternately pink, blue, brown, and green.

This vellum fragment, with its two colorful miniatures, is one of six excised from a Psalter in Prague (University Library, cod. XIV E 3) which still retains four figurative initials and a set of miniatures in the arches of its calendar pages.[7] Hanns Swarzenski has shown the Prague Psalter to be closely bound in style, iconography, text and codicology to a group of three other Psalters: London, Chester Beatty Library, cod. 40;[8] Munich, Staatsbibliothek, cod. lat. 16137;[9] and Nuremburg, Stadtbibliothek Solger, cod. I. 2. 4.°[10] The origin of this group is

Fig. 32a. 1:1

firmly linked to Augsburg since three of its members (excluding the Prague codex) carry the following October 28th calendar entry: "*Dedicatio matricis ecclesiae (in Augusta)*."[11] Further, they may be dated between 1234/1235 and 1255 since all four include references to Saints Dominic and Elizabeth, canonized on the former dates (respectively), and lack references to Saint Clare, canonized in 1255.[12]

The Prague Psalter is set somewhat apart by the fact that its calendar, although indicating the diocese of Augsburg, lacks the October 28th entry cited above and shows variant citations for twenty-one saint days.[13] Noting the inclusion of the *Translatio Benedicti* in its calendar, Swarzenski suggested that the Prague Psalter (and Rosenwald leaf) was produced in the Augsburg workshop for a Benedictine cloister within the diocese.[14]

Recently, A. H. van der Beek-Scheffer reexamined the saint entries of the Prague Psalter, especially the citation on October 11th of Burchart, a bishop of Worms (c. 1000).[15] Noting that the bishops of Worms and Augsburg were often among the entourage of Frederick II in the years 1234 to 1237; that Frederick was married at Worms in 1235; and that the luxurious decorative program of the Prague Psalter suggests a high-placed patron, Dr. van der Beek-Scheffer hypothesizes a link to the Emperor, who held court at Augsburg for several months in 1235. The Psalter may even, he suggests, have been intended as a gift from Frederick to Kunigunde, Queen of Bohemia, who acted as hostess at his Augsburg court while her husband, King Wenceslaus, was among the Emperor's most distinguished guests. No dedication picture nor inscription, however, supports this assumption.

1. Swarzenski, 1936, no. 59, pls. 724–726.
2. Swarzenski, 1936, no. 58, pls. 710, 731.
3. Swarzenski, 1936, no. 58, pls. 713–732.
4. van der Beek-Scheffer, 1969, 10, fig. 1; Sotheby and Co. [Sale Catalogue: Dec. 13, 1961] (London 1961), lot 194.
5. Swarzenski, 1936, no. 58, pls. 733–734.
6. *Mittelalterliche Kunst der Sammlung Kofler-Truniger, Luzern [Aachener Kunstblätter des Museumvereins 31*, (1965)] (Aachen 1965), no. M3, fig. p. 81.
7. See PARENT MANUSCRIPT and SISTER MINIATURES. The Rosenwald cutting was probably originally bound, along with its sister miniatures, before Psalm 1. Such is the case with the closely related Psalter in Nuremburg (Stadtbibliothek Solger, cod. I. 2. 4.°) (see note 10 below).
8. Swarzenski, 1936, no. 60, figs. 721–723, 727. Four figurative initials; 186 fols. (255 x 172 mm); 1 column of 17 lines.
9. Swarzenski, 1936, no. 61, figs. 714, 720, 728, 730, 737–742. Three figurative initials; 162 fols. (272 x 200 mm); 1 column of 18 lines.
10. Swarzenski, 1936, no. 62, figs. 711–712, 715–719, 729. Six full-page miniatures and three figurative initials; 151 fols. (230 x 170 mm); 1 column of 20 lines.
11. Swarzenski, 1936, I, p. 58.
12. Swarzenski, 1936, I, p. 58.
13. Swarzenski, 1936, no. 59. For a discussion of these saints see van der Beek-Scheffer, 1969, p. 11.
14. Swarzenski, 1936, no. 59. See van der Beek-Scheffer, 1969, 12 and note 21.
15. van der Beek-Scheffer, 1969, pp. 11f.

Fig. 32b. Verso, 1:1

Fig. 32c. *The Annunciation* (recto). Nuremberg,
Germanisches Nationalmuseum, cod. MM26

Fig. 32d. *The Nativity* (verso). Nuremberg, Germanisches
Nationalmuseum, cod. MM26

Fig. 32e. *The Adoration of the Magi* (recto). Nuremberg,
Landesgewerbemuseum, cod. v. 24 nr. 1925–1926

Fig. 32f. *The Presentation in the Temple* (verso).
Nuremberg, Landesgewerbemuseum, cod. v. 24 nr. 1925–1926

Fig. 32g. *The Betrayal* (recto). Nuremberg, Germanisches Nationalmuseum, cod. MM27

Fig. 32h. *Christ Carrying the Cross* (verso). Nuremberg, Germanisches Nationalmuseum, cod. MM27

Fig. 32i. *The Ascension* (recto). Lucerne, Kofler-Truniger Collection

Fig. 32j. *Majestas Domini* (verso). Lucerne, Kofler-Truniger Collection

33

Leaf from a Psalter

Paradise with Christ in the Lap of Abraham
Lower Saxony (Braunschweig?), 1239 (?)
B-13,521
224 X 157 (8 7/8 x 6 1/4)

Late thirteenth-century mixed Gothic minuscule and cursive;[1] text block: c. 130 mm wide (original?)

CONDITION (VG) Colors and facial details very fresh; gold slightly rubbed; numerous pin holes along top; haloes, throne, rivers, vases, tarnished; verso: R. Forrer stamp—Lugt suppl. 941a)

PROVENANCE By the fourteenth century in Hildesheim;[2] R. Forrer, Strasbourg (1904); E. Rosenthal, Berkeley; L. J. Rosenwald, Jenkintown (1946); National Gallery of Art (1946)

EXHIBITED *Medieval Book Paintings* (?) (San Francisco: M. H. de Young Museum, 1944); Baltimore, 1949, no. 33, illus.; Los Angeles, 1953–1954, no. 23; *The Year 1200: A Centennial Exhibition at The Metropolitan Museum of Art*, I (New York: The Metropolitan Museum of Art, 1970), no. 270, illus.; Trenton, 1971, no. 17; South Bend, 1972, no. 3.

BIBLIOGRAPHY Robert Forrer, *Strassburger Post*, Sept. 20, 1904; Arthur Haseloff, "Die Mittelalterliche Kunst," *Meisterwerke der Kunst aus Sachsen und Thüringen* (ed. Oscar Doering) (Magdeburg 1905), p. 98; Robert Forrer, *Unedierte Miniaturen, Federzeichnungen und Initialen des Mittelalters*, II (Strasbourg 1907), pp. 5, 8f., pl. VIII; Karl Wenk, "Die heilige Elisabeth und Papst Gregor IX," *Hochland 5, no. 2* (Nov. 1907), 129ff., illus.; Amédée Boinet, *La Collection de miniatures de M. Edouard Kann* (Paris 1926), p. 9f.; Paul Wescher, *Miniaturen-Handschriften und Einzeblätter—des Kupferstichkabinetts der Staatlichen Museen Berlin* (Leipzig 1931), p. 15. Hanns Swarzenski, *Die Lateinischen illuminierten Handschriften des XIII. Jahrhunderts in Ländern an Rhein, Main und Donau* (Berlin 1936), pp. 79f., 155n., 157n., 161n.; Erwin Rosenthal, "Abraham and Lazarus. Iconographical Considerations of a Medieval Book Painting," *The Pacific Art Review 4* (1945–1946), 7ff., illus.; Ernst Kantorowicz, "The Quinity of Winchester," *The Art Bulletin 29, no. 2* (June 1947), 85, fig. 11; Hans Gerstinger, "Über Herkunft und Entwicklung der anthropomorphen byzantinisch-slawischen Trinitätsdarstellung des sogenannten Synthronoi- und Paternitas (Otéchestow) Typus," *Festschrift W. Sas-Zaloziecky zum 60. Geburtstag* (Graz 1956), p. 81, n. 34; *Manuscrits à peintures offerts à la Bibliothèque Nationale par Comte Guy du Boisrouvray* (Paris 1961), p. 27f.; Renate Kroos, *Drei Niedersächsischen Bildhandschriften des 13. Jahrhunderts in Wien* (*Abhandlungen der Akademie der Wissenschaften in Göttingen, Philologische-Historische Klasse, dritte Folge, nr. 56*) (Göttingen 1964), pp. 88n., 185; Johannes Sommer, *Das Deckenbild der Michaelskirche zu Hildesheim* (Hildesheim 1965), p. 145; Johann-Christian Klamt, "Zum Arenberg-Psalter," *Munuscula Discipulorum: Kunsthistorische Studien Hans Kauffmann zum 70. Geburtstag 1966* (Berlin 1968), p. 152, fig. 105; A. H. van der Beek-Scheffer, "Nog twee miniaturen voor het Augsburgse psalter in Praag," *Miscellanea I. Q. van Regteren Altena, 16/v/1969* (Amsterdam 1969), p. 12; Robert Deshman, "Anglo-Saxon Art After Alfred," *The Art Bulletin 56, no. 2* (June 1974), 181f.

PARENT MANUSCRIPT Paris, Bibliothèque Nationale, cod. nouv. acq. lat. 3102: 157 folios (280 x 185 mm); Rosenwald miniature was located between folios 146 and 147 (*figs. 33c-33f*)[3]

SISTER MINIATURES
1) Glencoe, Illinois, Joel Spitz Collection: single leaf (225 x 150 mm); recto: Annunciation, Visitation, and Nativity (*fig. 33g*); verso: calendar for December (v)[4]
2) Chicago, Art Institute, cod. 24.671: single leaf (c. 225 x 160 mm); Flagellation and Crucifixion (*fig. 33h*)[5]
3) Berlin, Staatliche Museen, Stiftung Preussischer Kulturbesitz,

Fig. 33a. 1:1

Fig. 33c. *Frontispiece to the Litany of the Saints (the Deësis)* (fol. 147r). Paris, Bibliothèque Nationale, cod. NOUV. acq. lat. 3102

Fig. 33d. *The Presentation in the Temple, and the Adoration of the Magi* (fol. 7r). Paris, Bibliothèque Nationale, cod. NOUV. acq. lat. 3102

Kunstbibliothek: single leaf with ornamental initial D (Psalm 26) (*fig. 33i*)[6]

RECTO *(fig. 33b)* A late thirteenth-century copy of a letter from Pope Gregory IX to Elizabeth of Thuringia[7]

VERSO *(fig. 33a;* Colorplate VII) (Luke 16: 19-26) Abraham, with the Christ Child in his lap, is enthroned in paradise, symbolized by the "tree of life" in the background and nude personifications of the four rivers of paradise in the corners of the composition: Geon, Physon, Tygris, and Euphrates (Gen. 2:10). The "elect," several holding palm branches of martyrdom, are dressed in gaily colored contemporary secular garments; those of the lower row step forward to receive fruit from the hand of Christ (Rev. 2:7: ... to eat of the tree of life, which is in the midst of the paradise of God).

This leaf, along with at least two other fragments in American collections, was once part of a luxurious German thirteenth-century Psalter formerly in the collection of the Duke of Arenberg, now in the Bibliothèque Nationale, Paris.[8] According to codicological evidence,[9] the Paradise miniature served as frontispiece to the Litany of the Saints (which begins on folio 147r), where it would, in a general sense, represent the celestial reward of the "elect" recited in the following litany.[10]

There are several lines of evidence for the localization and dating of our miniature and its parent manuscript.[11] Renate Kroos has shown that its calendar generally indicates the bishoprics of Hildesheim and Magdeburg.[12] Further, July 7th carries the Feast of the *Translatio sancti Thomae episcopi* which was celebrated beginning in 1238 at

Fig. 33e. *The Entry into Jerusalem, and the Last Supper* (fol. 9v). Paris, Bibliothèque Nationale, cod. NOUV. acq. lat. 3102

Fig. 33f. *Initial B (Psalm 1)* (fol. 10v). Paris, Bibliothèque Nationale, cod. NOUV. acq. lat. 3102

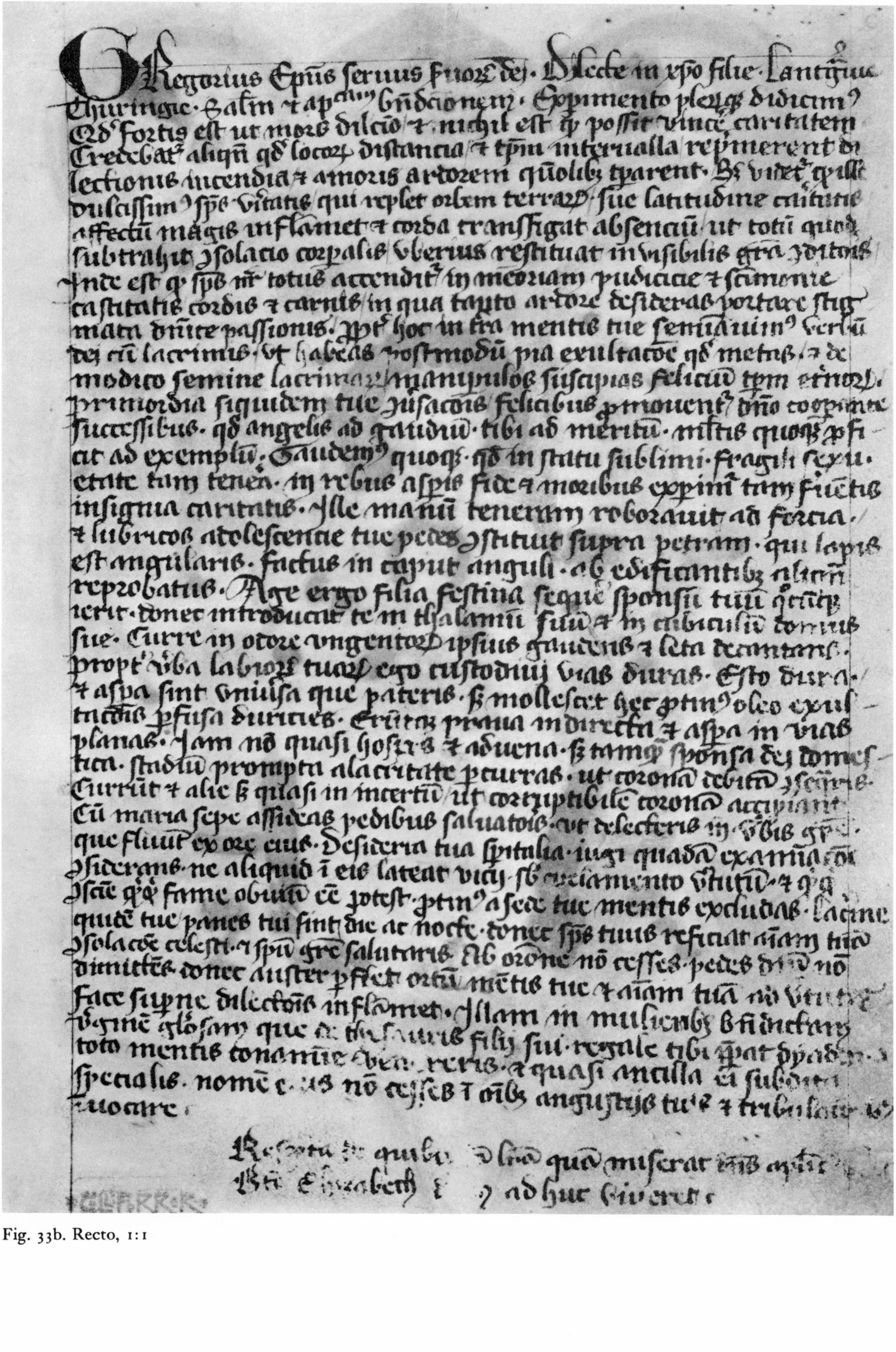

Gregorius Epus seruus seruorum dei. Dilecte in christo filie. Lantgrauie
Churingie. Salm z apca bndiaonem. Exprimento plerqz didicim
q fortis est ut mors dilcio z nichil est q possit uince caritatem
Credebat aliqn qd locoz distancia z tpm interualla reprimerent di-
lectionis incendia z amoris ardorem quolibz tparent. Z uidet q ille
dulcissim ihs ihus qui replet orbem terraz siue latitudine cristiane
affectu magis inflamet z corda transfigat absenciu ut totu quod
subtrahit ysolacio corpalis uberius restituat inuisibilis gra zdiuinus
vnde est q sps nr totus accendit in memoriam pudicicie z scimonie
castitatis cordis z carnis in qua tanto ardore desideras portare stigmata dnice passionis. ppt hoc in tra mentis tue seminauim verbu
dei cu lacrimis. ut habeas postmodu pia exultatoe qd metus. z de
modico semine lacrimaz manipulos sicapias felicius tpm ernoz.
primordia siquidem tue puisacois feliciabus pmouent dno cooperante
successibus. qd angelis ad gaudiu. tibi ad meritu. mistis quoqz pfi-
cit ad exemplu. Gaudem quoqz q in statu sublimi. fragili sexu
etate tam tenera in rebus aspis fide z moribus copiru tam fructe
insignia caritatis. Ille manu teneram roborauit ad fortia.
z lubricos atolescentie tue pedes ystituit supra petram. qui lapis
est angularis. factus in caput anguli. ab edificantibz aliorum
reprobatus. Age ergo filia festina sequre sponsu tuu qreuz
reuertit donec introducat te in thalamu suu z in cubiculu domus
sue. Curre in odore ungentoz ipsius gaudens z leta decantans.
propt uba labioz tuaz ego custodiui uias duras. Esto dura-
z aspa sint uniuersa que pateris. sz mollescat ergo ptinu oleo exul-
tacois pfusa durities. Eritqz preuia in directu z aspa in uias
planas. Iam no quasi hospes z aduena. sz tamqz sponsa dei domes-
tica. stadiu prompta alacritate pcurras. ut corona debita ysequris.
Currit z alie sz quasi in incertu. ut corruptibile corona accipiant.
cu maria sepe assideas pedibus saluatois. ut delecteris in ubis q
que fluut ex ore eius. Desideria tua spiritalia. iugi quadam examinacoe
ysiderans. ne aliquid in eis lateat uicii sb obtentamento uirtutu z qo
istet qd fame obuitu ee potest. ptinus a seca tue mentis excludas. la qne
quite tue panes tui sint die ac nocte. donec sps tuus reficiat aiam tua
ysolacoe celesti. z spu gre salutaris. ab oratione no cesses. pedes dni no
face sz ipse dileccois inflamet. Illam in musicus bndictam
virgine gloriam que a thesauris filii sui regale tibi pparat pprium z
toto mentis conamine ueneris. z quasi ancilla eu subdita
specialis. nome eius no cessebi in oibz angustiis tue z tribulacoe ui
uocare.

Recepta de quibus dlcoq que miserat etc etc
Bta Elizabeth z q adhuc uiuerut

Fig. 33b. Recto, 1:1

Fig. 33g. *The Annunciation, Visitation, and Nativity*. Glencoe, Illinois, Joel Spitz Collection

Fig. 33h. *The Flagellation and Crucifixion*. Chicago, Art Institute, cod. 24.671

the Saint Blasius foundation in Braunschweig (Thomas of Canterbury was a patron saint), which until 1256 belonged to Hildesheim. Moreover, March 27th is marked as Easter Sunday, a circumstance which occurred in the thirteenth century only in 1239 and 1250.[13] Finally, the recto of the Rosenwald leaf bears the already mentioned late thirteenth-century copy of a letter from Pope Gregory IX to Saint Elizabeth of Thuringia (who died in 1231 and was canonized in 1235). In 1238 the same pope, wrote a letter to Duke Otto of Braunschweig granting dispensation for the marriage of his daughter Helen to the only son of Saint Elizabeth, Landgraf Hermann II of Thuringia. Johann-Christian Klamt has suggested that this luxurious Psalter was commissioned (perhaps by Otto or Hermann) for that wedding, which took place on October 9, 1239. He speculates that the original document from which the transcription on our leaf was made (in the later thirteenth century), must have been a precious possession of the Landgraf House, that it may have passed at Hermann II's death in 1241 to Helen († 1273), and that she or a later owner may have arranged for its transcription into the Psalter.

Stylistically, the Arenberg Psalter (with its excised leaves) belongs to Haseloff's Saxon-Thuringian School,[14] where it is the most luxurious representative of an iconographically and stylistically closely interrelated sub-group,[15] which includes three other Psalters: Berlin, Kupferstichkabinett, cod. 78 A 7;[16] Wolfenbüttel, cod. Helmst. 515;[17] and Donaueschingen, Fürstl. Fürstenbergische Hofbibliothek, cod. 309.[18] In a broader sense the Arenberg Psalter is closely dependent on two luxurious Saxon-Thuringian Psalters datable to the 1210s: the so-called Landgraf Psalter (Stuttgart, Landesbibliothek cod. H. B. II. fol. 24);[19] and the Elizabeth Psalter in Cividale (Museo Archeologico Nazionale, cod. CXXXVII).[20] Klamt has suggested that the four members of the "Arenberg Group" all date around 1239, and that the Arenberg Psalter itself was based on a model from the Landgraf Psalter workshop.[21]

The Rosenwald miniature, a representation of paradise, is based on the parable of Lazarus and Dives (Luke 16: 19-26).[22] Compositionally, it may ultimately be derived from fuller narrative representations of the Lazarus and Dives parable traceable in both Byzantine and Western art,[23] although it also corresponds morphologically to representations of the Virgin and Child, and of Christ in the lap of God the Father.[24] More immediately, our scene is closely related to its counterpart in the Landgraf Psalter (fol. 175v), which precedes the Office of the Dead,[25] and in another Saxon-Thuringian Psalter in Wolfenbüttel (cod. Helmst. 568, fol. 9r), where it precedes Psalm 1.[26] The only significant difference is that in neither case does the figure in Abraham's lap have a cross nimbus. This addition in the Rosenwald illumination substitutes Christ for Lazarus as the source and symbol of celestial reward.

1. See Klamt, 1968, n. 23.
2. Manuscripts, 1961, 27; Klamt, 1968, n. 24.
3. Manuscripts, 1961, no. 4, pls. III, 4–9.
4. Boinet, 1926, no. I, pl. I.
5. Forrer, 1907, 8, pl. XI.
6. Klamt, 1968, 147ff., fig. 103.
7. See Wenk, 1907, passim (with transcription and translation); and Klamt, 1968, pp. 152ff.

Fig. 33i. *Initial D* (Psalm 26). Berlin, Staatliche Museen, Stiftung Preussischer Kulturbesitz

8. See PARENT MANUSCRIPT and SISTER MINIATURES above.

9. Manuscripts, 1961, p. 28.

10. Deshman (1974), 182) discusses the original location of the Rosenwald leaf and its iconographic ties to the litany that followed it. He emphasizes the connection between the Litany of the Saints and The Last Judgment, pointing out the fact that two frequent motifs of Last Judgment iconography, Abraham with a "Christ-like soul" in his lap, and the Deësis, are conspicuous features of the Rosenwald miniature and the leaf it originally faced (fol. 147r).

11. For these arguments see Klamt, 1968, pp. 152ff.

12. Kroos, 1964, p. 185n.

13. It was apparently on this evidence that Paul Clemen dated the Psalter to 1239 in the 1904 Düsseldorf exhibition catalogue [*Katalog der Kunsthistorischen Ausstellung* (Düsseldorf 1904), p. 184]. Several scholars have expressed doubt regarding the value of that dating (e.g. Manuscrits, 1961, 27; Kroos, 1964, p. 185n).

14. Arthur Haseloff, *Eine Thüringisch-sächsische Malerschule des 13. Jahrhunderts* (Strasbourg 1897), passim. (The Arenberg Psalter was not known to Haseloff.)

15. See Klamt, 1968, pp. 149ff.

16. Haseloff, 1897, p. 20, no. VII.

17. Haseloff, 1897, p. 21, no. VIII.

18. Haseloff, 1897, p. 18, no. VI.

19. Karl Löffler, *Der Landgrafenpsalter* (Leipzig 1925), passim. See also Kroos, 1964, p. 88n.

20. Gian Carlo Menis and Giuseppe Bergamini, *La Miniatura in Friuli* (Udine: Palazzo Comunale, 1972), no. 8, illus. pp. 67–75.

21. Klamt, 1968, p. 154.

22. For a treatment of the relevant visual and textual sources, see Rosenthal, 1945–1946, 7ff.; and Gérard Cames, *Allégories et symboles dans l'Hortus Deliciarum* (Leiden 1971), pp. 124ff., fig. 129.

23. Rosenthal, 1945–1946, 10ff., esp. figs. pp. 10, 13. Abraham with Lazarus (or a group of souls) in his bosom had also been absorbed as a frequent motif in Last Judgment scenes, where it represented Paradise (Deshman, 1974, 182).
A representation of Abraham enthroned in a quatrefoil frame is found in an eleventh-century English Psalter, Vatican Library, cod. reg. lat. 12 [Francis Wormald, *English Drawings of the 10th and 11th Centuries* (London 1952), pl. 26]. Abraham enthroned, framed by the four rivers of paradise, occurs in the *Hortus Deliciarum*, and in Munich, Staatsarchiv, Necrology, fol. 74v (Cames, 1971, figs. 129, 131).

24. Gerstinger, 1956, p. 81.

25. Löffler, 1925, pl. XX. (It immediately follows the litany.)

26. Rosenthal, 1945–1946, fig. p. 8.

34

Leaf from a Psalter

Pentecost

Lower Saxony (vicinity of Goslar?), mid-13th century

B-22,224

194 x 133 (7 5/8 x 5 1/4)

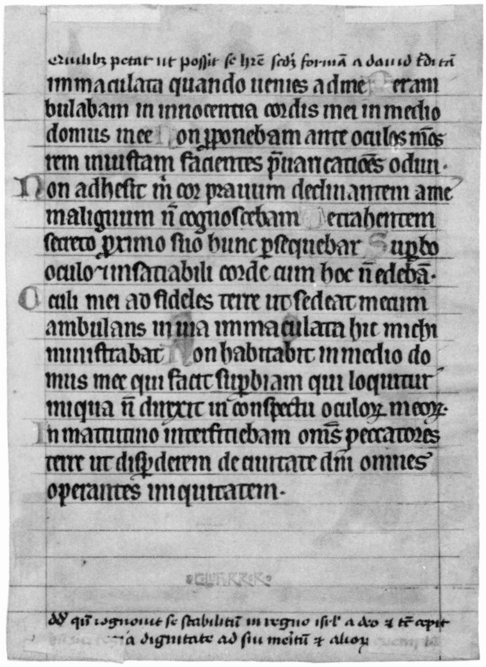
equalibus petat ut possit se hec scilicet formam a dauid editam

immaculata quando uenies ad me. eram
bulabam in innocentia cordis mei in medio
domus mee. on proponebam ante oculos meos
rem iniustam facientes preuaricationes odiui.
Non adhesit michi cor prauum declinantem a me
malignum non cognoscebam. etrahentem
secreto proximo suo hunc persequebar. uperbo
oculo et insatiabili corde cum hoc non edebam.
Oculi mei ad fideles terre ut sedeant mecum
ambulans in uia immaculata hic michi
ministrabat. on habitabit in medio do
mus mee qui facit superbiam qui loquitur
iniqua non direxit in conspectu oculorum meorum.
In matutino interficiebam omnes peccatores
terre ut disperderem de ciuitate domini omnes
operantes iniquitatem.

Fig. 34b. Recto

Early Gothic minuscule script; 1 column of 20 lines (16 filled) (155 x 101 mm)

CONDITION (E) Colors and detail very fresh; little sign of flaking or rubbing; trimmed all around (verso: one line of semi-cursive script in upper margin, two in lower margin; R. Forrer stamp—Lugt suppl. 941a)

PROVENANCE Still part of parent manuscript in 1876;[1] Kahlert/Eisenach (by 1905); R. Forrer, Strasbourg; M. Wertheimer; L. J. Rosenwald, Jenkintown (1957); National Gallery of Art (1961)

EXHIBITED South Bend, 1972, no. 5, illus.

BIBLIOGRAPHY Arthur Haseloff, "Die Mittelalterliche Kunst," *Meisterwerke der Kunst aus Sachsen und Thüringen* (ed. Oscar Doering) (Magdeburg 1905), p. 106; Renate Kroos, *Drei Niedersächsischen Bildhandschriften des 13. Jahrhunderts in Wien (Abhandlungen der Akademie der Wissenschaften in Göttingen, Philologische-Historische Klasse, dritte Folge, nr. 56)* (Göttingen 1964), p. 83f.; Renate Kroos, *Niedersächsische Bildstichereien des Mittelalters* (Berlin 1970), p. 65n.; Renate Kroos, "Beiträge zur Niedersächsischen Buchmalerei des 13. Jahrhundert," *Die Diözese Hildesheim in Vergangenheit und Gegenwart 40* (1972) 117ff

PARENT MANUSCRIPT Hildesheim, Dombibliothek/Beverinsche Bibliothek, cod. J 26: Rosenwald miniature originally preceded Psalm 101 (102), thus serving as frontispiece to the third division of Psalms[2]

RECTO *(fig. 34b)* Ps. 100:2 (101:2): *immaculata, quando venies ...*, through Ps. 100:8 (the end).

VERSO *(fig. 34a)* (Acts 2:1-4) The Virgin, whose presence is not mentioned in the Biblical account, is enthroned in the midst of the Apostles. Crowned, she wears a deep blue mantle over a gold tunic. Peter, heading the Apostles on the left, is dressed in bright red over green, while Paul, at the right, is in bright red over light blue. The architectural frame, from which descends the white Dove of the Holy Spirit, is rendered in shades of bright red, green, blue, salmon, and beige; the background is highly burnished gold.

This trimmed single leaf was, until at least the later nineteenth century, part of a thirteenth-century North German Psalter in Hildesheim (Dombibliothek/Beverinsche Bibliothek, cod. J 26).[3] Since Psalm 100 (101 in the King James Version) is concluded on the recto of this leaf, the Pentecost scene of its verso would originally have faced the beginning of Psalm 101: Hear my prayer, O Lord, and let my cry come unto thee....

According to Renate Kroos, who first associated the Rosenwald leaf with its parent manuscript, this Pentecost iconography follows North Saxon types prevalent from c. 1170. Thus the Virgin, whose presence is not mentioned in the Biblical account, wears a crown and tunic of gold, reflecting local sermons which describe the Mother of Christ as a golden-robed queen.[4] She notes that this type of Pentecost, with the Virgin flanked by two groups of Apostles, may be found in several North Saxon manuscripts.

The localization of the Hildesheim Psalter, and those manuscripts to which it is most closely related, is uncertain. Kroos questions the significance of the Hildesheim provenance, since the litanies in a number of manuscripts of the group omit significant Hildesheim saints, and when those saints are mentioned in the text, their names are not emphasized in red. Dr. Kroos suggests instead that hagio-

Fig. 34a: 1:1

graphical evidence points toward a location within the Archbishopric
of Mainz, in the vicinity of Goslar (if not Goslar itself).[5]

1. Kroos, 1964, p. 83n.
2. Kroos, 1972, passim.
3. See PARENT MANUSCRIPT; Kroos, 1972, pp. 129ff.
4. Kroos, 1972, p. 131.
5. Kroos, 1972, p. 131.

35

Initial A from a Martyrology with the Rule of Saint Benedict

The Virgin and Child Enthroned, and Saint Benedict Imparting His Rule

Upper Rhine, second half 13th century

B-15,391

159 x 121 (6 5/16 x 4 3/4)

Early Gothic minuscule script; 1 column of 15 lines with traces of a 16th (incomplete); column c. 120 mm wide

CONDITION (E) Colors and detail very fresh; several minor abrasions; trimmed on all sides (verso: R. Forrer stamp—Lugt suppl. 941a)

PROVENANCE R. Forrer, Strasbourg; E. Rosenthal, Berkeley; L. J. Rosenwald, Jenkintown (1949); National Gallery of Art (1949)

EXHIBITED National Gallery, 1950, no. 7; Trenton, 1971, no. 14

BIBLIOGRAPHY Hanns Swarzenski, *Die Lateinischen illuminierten Handschriften des XIII. Jahrhunderts in Ländern an Rhein, Main und Donau* (Berlin 1936), p. 53, no. 47, fig. 584

SISTER MINIATURES
1) Munich, Staatliche Graphische Sammlung, cod. 40258: single miniature (127 x 124 mm); the Nativity (*fig. 35c*)[1]
2) Munich, Staatliche Graphische Sammlung, cod. 40259: single miniature (122 x 126 mm); Death of the Virgin (*fig. 35d*)[2]
3) Formerly: Munich, J. Rosenthal Collection: single miniature (180 x 130 mm); Crucifixion with Saint Benedict (*fig. 35e*)[3]

RECTO (*fig. 35a*) Beginning of the Prologue to the Rule of Saint Benedict: *Ausculta* [*o fili, praecepta*].[4] (Harken, my son, to the precepts of the master and incline the ear of thy heart. . . .) The Virgin, who wears beige over light blue, embraces the Christ Child, dressed in dark green. Saint Benedict, carrying a crozier, imparts his rule (represented by a long banderole) to a group of six monks. All are tonsured and dressed in black Benedictine habits. The dark blue background is spotted with gold diamonds; the initial is gold and frames areas of light pink and dark green.

VERSO (*fig. 35b*) Continuation (after a gap of ten words) of the Prologue (verse 1): [*admo*]*ni*[*tion*]*em pii Patris* . . . (to verse 6) . . . *ei om*[*n*]*i tem*[*pore*].

This historiated initial A, marking the beginning of the Prologue to the Benedictine Rule, was probably once part of a single manuscript

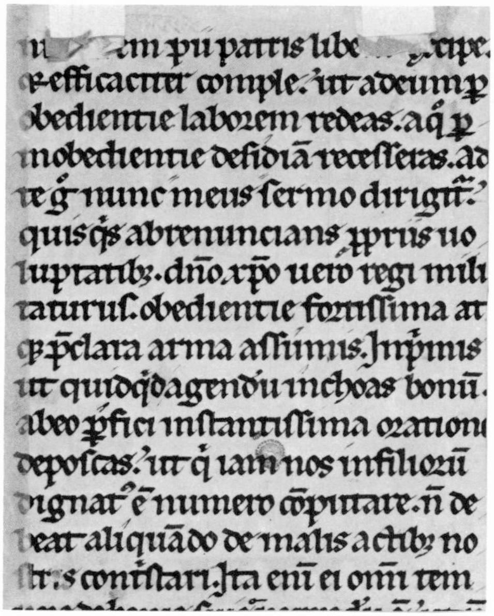
n... em pii patris libe... ecipe.
e efficaciter comple. ut ad eum p
obedientie laborem redeas. a q p
inobedientie desidiā recesseras. ad
te ergo nunc meus sermo dirigitur.
quisquis abrenuncians ppriis uo
luptatibus. dño xpo uero regi mili
taturus. obedientie fortissima at
q pclara arma assumis. In primis
ut quicquid agendū inchoas bonū.
ab eo pfici instantissima oratione
deposcas. ut qui iam nos in filiorū
dignatus est numero computare. n de
beat aliquādo de malis actibus no
stris contristari. Ita enī ei omī tem

Fig. 35b. Verso

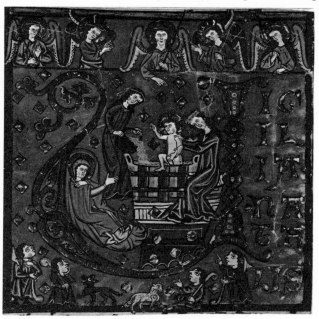

Fig. 35c. *The Nativity*. Munich, Staatliche Graphische Sammlung, cod. 40258

Fig. 35a. 1:1

with two miniatures in the Staatliche Graphische Sammlung, Munich (cods. 40258 and 40259), and a single Crucifixion miniature, formerly in the Jacques Rosenthal Collection, Munich.[5] Together they would have helped comprise a Martyrology (a collection of short narratives on the passions of martyrs, read at the Office of Prime), coupled with the Rule of Saint Benedict. That this manuscript was intended for a Benedictine monastery is apparent not only from the inclusion of the Rule, but also from the prominent position granted Saint Benedict in the Crucifixion miniature.

Hanns Swarzenski, who first associated these four cuttings (although mistakenly identified the monk as Saint Dominic), dated them to the second half of the thirteenth century, and localized them to the Upper Rhine.[6] The golden rinceaux decoration of the Rosenwald initial, with its trefoil leaves, is not usually found in manuscripts of this period. It resembles that of Ottonian initials and suggests an eleventh-century model.

1. Swarzenski, 1936, no. 47, pl. 583.
2. Swarzenski, 1936, no. 47, pls. *586, 586*[1].
3. Swarzenski, 1936, no. 47, pl. 585.
4. Rudolphus Hanslik, *Benedicti Regula (Corpus scriptorum ecclesiasticorum latinorum: 75)* (Vienna 1960), p. 1f.
5. See SISTER MINIATURES.
6. Swarzenski, 1936, no. 47.

Fig. 35d. *The Death of the Virgin.* Munich, Staatliche Graphische Sammlung, cod. 40259

Fig. 35e. *The Crucifixion with Saint Benedict.* Formerly: Munich, J. Rosenthal Collection

36

Leaf from a Choir Book (Gradual)

Coronation of the Virgin with Attendant Saints
Cologne, second quarter 14th century, follower of Johannes von Valkenburg

B-21,292

435 X 309   (17 3/16 X 12 1/16)

Gothic minuscule script, with four–line staff in red (22 mm); 8 lines, each accompanied by a staff (308 x 204 mm)

CONDITION   (VG) Pigment and detail of initial very well preserved as is marginalia, except for area along bottom which shows rubbing and flaking; right edge scalloped as a result of removal from its binding

PROVENANCE   E. Rosenthal, Berkeley; L. J. Rosenwald, Jenkintown (1953); National Gallery of Art (1954)

EXHIBITED   Trenton, 1971, no. 20, illus.; South Bend, 1972, no. 10, illus.

RECTO   Remainder of the Alleluia for the Feast of Saint Francis (Oct. 4): *alleluja. hic Franciscus pauper* . . . ; followed by abbreviated instructions for the remainder of the Saint Francis mass; and a Common for a confessor bishop.

VERSO *(figs. 36a, 36b)*   Rubrics for the remainder of the service on the recto; rubrics for the feasts of Oct. 18, 27 (Vigil), 28, and 31 (Vigil); beginning of the Introit for the Feast of All Saints (Nov. 1): *Gaudeamus omnes in Domino* . . . (to) . . . *rectos decet lauda[tio]*. (Let us all rejoice in the Lord, celebrating a festival day in honor of all the Saints. . . .)

Christ is dressed in a gray mantle over a beige tunic; the Virgin is in beige over dark bluish green. The undifferentiated group of male and female saints below wear garments of red, brown, dark blue, and gray. The initial is beige with gold filler; the background is dark blue. The marginal ornament is also predominantly beige and dark blue, with terminating leaves in red, green, and blue. In addition to the droleries (which include a hybrid monk in a gray habit balancing a saucer on a stick), there is a praying Franciscan Nun (order of Poor Clares) to the left of the initial, wearing brown over gray.

This single leaf was excised from a choir book of the type produced for the monasteries of Cologne during the first half of the fourteenth century.[1] Several dozen manuscripts and fragments in this mode have been grouped around Johannes von Valkenburg, a monk who, in 1299, wrote and illuminated two Graduals for the use of his own Franciscan cloister in Cologne.[2] In adapting the style of northern French and Flemish models of the later thirteenth century, Valkenburg introduced Gothic illumination to Cologne and established a style and format of manuscript decoration that was to be perpetuated among various followers to the mid-fourteenth century.

The presence of a kneeling Franciscan nun in the margin (as well as the liturgical emphasis afforded Saint Francis on the recto), indicate that the Rosenwald leaf's parent manuscript was one of a substantial number of codices produced in and for the convent of Saint Clare, founded in Cologne in 1304.[3]

In figure, script, and ornament style our miniature stands apart from the Valkenburg Graduals of 1299.[4] Instead, it bears comparison with products of the second quarter of the century including three Missals in Darmstadt (Hessische Landes- und Hochschulbibliothek, cods. 837, 874, and 876),[5] and an Antiphony partly in Stockholm (Kungl. Biblioteket, cod. holm. A 172) and partly in Cologne (Wallraf-Richartz-Museum, Graphische Sammlung, cods. 65, 66), written and illuminated by the Franciscan nun Loppa de Speculo in 1350.[6]

Among the numerous similar choir book fragments showing

Franciscan nuns in the margins,[7] the most closely related are single leaves in Aachen (Suermondt-Museum) and Hanover (Kestner-Museum, cod. 3987), both apparently excised from a single codex.[8]

1. See Georg Graf Vitzthum, *Die Pariser Miniaturmalerei* (Leipzig 1907), p. 196ff.; Hermann Knaus, "Johann von Valkenburg und seine Nachfolger," *Archiv für Geschichte des Buchwesens 3, nos. 1–3* (1960), 58ff. [with earlier bibliography]; Eberhard Galley, "Noch einige Bemerkungen zur Kölner Buchmalerei der Gotik," *Archiv für Geschichte des Buchwesens 3, nos. 4–6* (1960), 582ff.; *Vor Stefan Lochner: Die Kölner Maler von 1300 bis 1430* (Cologne: Wallraf-Richartz-Museum, 1974), pp. 59ff. ["Zur Buchmalerei" by Gisela Plotzek-Wederhake], and entries 69–80.
2. Cologne, Erzbischöfliche Diözesanbibliothek, cod. 1b; and Bonn, Universitäts-bibliothek, cod. 384. See Cologne, 1974, no. 69, illus. pp. 127, 187.
3. See Cologne, 1974, 62f.; Eberhard Galley, "Miniaturen aus dem Kölner Klarissenkloster," *Aus der Welt des Bibliothekars: Festschrift für Rudolf Juchhoff zum 65. Geburtstag* (Cologne 1959), pp. 20ff.
4. See note 2.
5. Cologne, 1974, no. 78, illus. p. 135; Knaus, 1960, figs. 1–3. We would like to thank Gisela Plotzek-Wederhake for a very informative letter of August 3, 1974, regarding the Rosenwald fragment and its closest relatives. Ms. Plotzek-Wederhake is preparing a corpus of fourteenth-century Cologne manuscript painting.
6. Galley, 1959, pp. 20ff.; Cologne, 1974, p. 63, nos. 79–80, illus. pp. 137–139. Two leaves from that codex are in Cologne.
7. Dr. J. J. G. Alexander, in a letter of June 18, 1974, kindly provided important information regarding choir book fragments related to the Rosenwald leaf.
8. Also apparently from the same choir book are several single leaves in Cologne (Wallraf-Richartz-Museum, Graphische Sammlung, cods. 64, 67–71). We would like to thank Ms. Gisela Plotzek-Wederhake for details on the Cologne leaves. See Curt Weigelt, "Rheinische Miniaturen," *Wallraf-Richartz Jahrbuch 1* (1924), 10ff., figs. 4–5.

Fig. 36b. Verso, detail, 1:1

Fig. 36a

37

Leaf and Bifolio from a Bible

Moses counting the Children of Israel (A)
Joshua before the Lord (B)
Northern France (Arras?),
C. 1270
B-13,517 (A); B-13,516 (B)
Average: 484 x 353
(19 1/16 x 13 7/8)

Gothic minuscule script; 2 columns of 30 lines (average: 334 x 225 mm)

CONDITION   (VG) Colors and facial detail very well preserved; gold slightly rubbed; lower margin soiled; A trimmed along top; 80 mm slash in lower left of B; A numbered *11* upper, lower right; B, 1r numbered *17* in lower right; B, 2r numbered *18* upper right, *19* lower right

PROVENANCE   G. Stroganoff; E. Rosenthal, Berkeley; L. J. Rosenwald, Jenkintown (1946); National Gallery of Art (1946)

EXHIBITED   Trenton, 1971, no. 16

BIBLIOGRAPHY   Robert Branner, "A Cutting from a Thirteenth-Century French Bible," *The Bulletin of the Cleveland Museum of Art 58* (Sept. 1971), 221ff., fig. 7; Ellen J. Beer, "Liller Bibelcodices, Tournai und das Scriptorium der Stadt Arras," *Aachener Kunstblätter 43* (1972), 226

SISTER MINIATURES

1) Cambridge, Mass., Harvard College Library, cod. Typ 119: six single leaves (487 x 344 mm; text block: 340 x 230 mm; 30 lines per page); initial I with the seven days of creation, and the Crucifixion (Gen. 1:1 (*fig. 37e*)[1]

Fig. 37c. Recto, A, detail, 1:1

locutus qʒ
est dūs ad
moysen in
deserto sy
nai in ta
bernaculo
federis pri
ma die mensis secundi: anno
altero egressionis eorum er egi
pto dicens. Tollite summā uni
uerse congregationis filiorum
isrl̃ p cognationes ꝫ domos su
as. ꝫ nomina singuloꝝ quicꝗd
sexus est masculini a uicesimo
anno ꝫ supra. oĩum uiroꝝum
fortium ex isrl̃: et numerabitis
eos p turmas suas tu ꝫ aaron.
Eruntqʒ uobiscum principes tri
buum ac domoꝝ in cognatio
nibʒ suis: quoꝝum ista sunt
nomina. De tribu ruben: elisⁱ
filius sedeur. De symeon: sala
miel filius surisaddai. De iu
da: naason filius aminadab.
De ysachar: nathanabel filius
suar. De zabulon: eliab filius
helon. filioꝝ autem ioseph de ef
fraim: elisama filius ammiud.
De manasse: gamaliel filius
phadassur. De beniamin: abi

dan filius gedeonis. De dan: ah
iezer filius ammisaddai. De aser:
phegihel filius ochran. De gad: eli
asaph filius duhel. De neptali: a
hira filius enan. Hi nobilissimi
principes multitudinis p tribʒ ꝫ
cognationes suas et capita exerci
tus isrl̃. quos tulerunt moyses
ꝫ aaron cum omni uulgi mul
titudine: et congregauerunt pri
mo die mensis secundi. recensen
tes eos p cognationes et domos
ac familias et capita ꝫ nomina
singuloꝝ a uicesimo anno et
supra. sicut preceperat dūs mo
ysi. Numeratiqʒ sunt in deser
to syna · De ruben primogeni
to isrlis. p generationes ꝫ famili
as ac domos suas et nomina
capitum singuloꝝ. omne quod
sexus est masculini. a uicesimo
anno et supra. procedentium ad
bellum: quadraginta sex milia
quingenti. De filiis symeon. p
generationes et familias ac do
mos cognationum suaꝝ recen
siti sunt p nomina et capita sin
guloꝝ. omne quod sexus est ma
sculini a uicesimo anno ꝫ supra
procedentium ad bellum: quinꝗ

2) Formerly: New York, H. P. Kraus: single leaf (474 x 360 mm; text block 337 x 226 mm; 30 lines per page); Moses Sacrificing (Lev. 1:1)[2]

3) Philadelphia, Museum of Art, cod. 46.65.1: single leaf (481 x 350 mm; text block: 333 x 226 mm; 30 lines per page); the Lord speaks to Judah (Judg. 1:1) *(fig. 37f)*[3]

A, RECTO *(figs. 37a, 37c)* Num. 1:1—Num. 1:23. *Locutusq[ue]/ est/d[omi]n[u]s ad Moysen in deserto Sinai. . . .* (And the Lord spoke unto Moses in the wilderness of Sinai . . . saying, Take ye the sum of all the children of Israel. . . .)

   Moses, with his symbolic horns, is dressed in a dark blue mantle over a red tunic. The garments of the group he addresses are dark blue, brown, red, and gray; each figure wears the Jewish pointed hat. The Lord appears out of a small blue cloud at the upper left. The body of the initial is blue and light beige.

A, VERSO Num. 1:23—Num. 1:38 (. . . *ad bella/p[ro]cedere*).

B, 1 RECTO Deut. 31:21 (*sit hodie . . .*)—Deut. 32:8.

B, 1 VERSO Deut. 32:9—Deut. 32:26 (. . . *memoriam eoru[m]*).

B, 2 RECTO Jerome's Prologue to Joshua, beginning with the forty-first word (*monemusq[ue] lectorum . . .*).

B, 2 VERSO *(figs. 37b, 37d)* End of Jerome's Prologue; followed by another (9-line) prologue; Josh. 1:1—Josh. 1:8 (. . . *que scripta sunt*). *Et factum est ut post mortem Moysi servi D[omi]ni, loqueretur D[omi]n[u]s ad Iosue. . . .* (Now after the death of Moses the servant of the Lord it came to pass, that the Lord spoke unto Joshua. . . .)

Fig. 37d. Verso, B, detail, 1:1

Ceterum post scē paule dormitionē.
cuius uita uirtutis exemplum ē.
⁊ hos libros quos custochie uirgi
ni xpī negare non potui. decreui
mus dum spiritus hos regit ar
tus. ꝓphetarum explanationi in
cumbere ⁊ et omissum iam diu
opus quasi quodam postlimini
o repetere: presertim cum evadmi
rabilis scūs q̄ uir pammachius hoc
idem litteris flagitet. ⁊ nos ad pa
triam festinantes. mortiferos syre
narum cantus. surda debeamus
aure transire. Item alius ꝓlogus.
hesus filius naue in typum dūi
non solum in gestis uerum et no
mine: transiordanē hostium reg
na subiunt. Diuidit terram uicto
ri populo: et ꝑ singulas urbes iu
cilos. montes. flumina. torrentes
atq̄ confinia. ecclie celestis q̄ ihe
rusalem spiritualia regna deseri
bit. Explicit ꝓlogus. Incipit liber
iosue.

factum
est ut post
mortem
moysi ser
ui dūi lo
quertur

dūs ad iosue filium nun. mini
strum moysi: et diceret ei. Moyses
seruus meus mortuus est: surge
⁊ transi iordanem istum. tu ⁊ omnis
ppls tecum. in terram quam ego
dabo filijs isrl. Omnē locum quē
calcauerit uestigium pedis uestri
uobis tradam ⁊ sicut locutus sū
moysi. Adeserto ⁊ libano usq̄ ad
flumen magnum eufraten. ois
terra etheorum usq̄ ad mare ma
gnum contra solis occasum: erit
terminus uester. Nullus uobis
poterit resistere ⁊ cunctis diebus
uite tue. Sicut fui cum moyse ⁊
ero ⁊ tecum. Non dimittam nec
derelinquā te: confortare ⁊ esto ro
bustus. Tu enim sorte diuides po
pulo huic terram. ꝑ qua iuraui
patrib; tuis. ut traderem eam il
lis. Confortare igitur ⁊ esto robu
stus ualde ⁊ ut custodias ⁊ facias
omnē legem quam precepit t̄ mo
yses seruus meus. Ne declines ab
ea ad dexteram uel ad sinistram:
ut intelligas cuncta que agis. Nō
recedat uolumen legis huius de
ore tuo ⁊ sed meditaberis in eo di
eb; ac nochb;: ut custodias et
facias omnia que scripta siunt

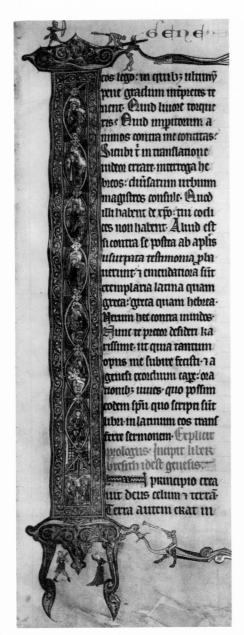

Fig. 37e. *Initial I with the Seven Days of Creation, and the Crucifixion.* Cambridge, Mass., Harvard College Library, cod. Typ. 119 (detail)

The Lord is dressed in a brown mantle over a dark blue tunic; Joshua is in gray over red. The core of the initial is blue, its inner field highly burnished gold, and its framing field light reddish brown.

These three folios, with their historiated incipit initials for the Books of Numbers and Joshua, were excised from a large, deluxe Bible of the type produced in northern France during the second half of the thirteenth century.[4] Robert Branner, who was able to identify eight sister folios with three additional incipit miniatures,[5] has named the as yet untraced parent manuscript the Hofer Bible, since its Genesis initial is in the Philip Hofer Collection at Harvard.

While Parisian scriptoria of the second half of the thirteenth century usually specialized in Bibles of the smaller, more handy, "university" type, large-sized Bibles bound in four or more volumes[6] continued to be produced for monastic use in northern France. According to a recent survey by Branner, a number of interrelated copies were written and illuminated in that area during the 1260s and 1270s; all in a similar script, aligned in the columns of 26, 30, or 31 lines, and containing historiated initials executed in the (comparatively) linear style and restricted color scheme typical of the region.[7] In a series of articles Ellen Beer has located the main center for the production of these Bibles in Arras, and has isolated a number of illuminators within the scriptorium of Johannes Philomena.[8]

The abundant use of gold, the inflected, tapering figures, the angular drapery, and the expressive physiognomies combine to place the Hofer Bible miniatures stylistically near the end of the group. They contrast with the broader mode exhibited in the Glazier Bible (New York, Pierpont Morgan Library, cod. Glazier 64),[9] the Bible in Lille (Bibliothèque Municipale, cod. 835-838), datable to 1264,[10] and the Bible fragment in Brussels (Bibliothèque Royale, cod. II.2523).[11]

Closer in style to the Rosenwald initials are those in the Marquette Bible (New York, H. P. Kraus), a product of the Johannes Philomena scriptorium in which Ellen Beer has recently distinguished six hands;[12] a fragmentary Psalter in the Bodleian Library, Oxford (cod. laud. lat. 85),[13] and the initials from a Bible in Arras (Bibliothèque Municipale, cod. 1 [olim 3]).[14]

1. *Illuminated and Calligraphic Manuscripts* (Cambridge, Mass.: Fogg Art Museum and Houghton Library, 1955), no. 26, pl. 15.
2. H. P. Kraus, *Thirty-Five Manuscripts* [Sale Catalogue no. 100, 1962] (New York 1962), no. 7, pls. x–xi.
The Kraus catalogue suggests that the Leviticus folio was originally part of a Bible, two volumes of which are in Brussels (Bibliothèque Municipale, cod. II. 2523). While the size and make-up of the Rosenwald leaves and their sister folios are close to the Brussels manuscript their miniature style is more refined, their use of extenders less lavish, and their dimensions smaller (the Brussels codex measures 498 x 357 mm). See Camille Gaspar and Frédéric Lyna, *Les Principaux manuscrits à peintures de la Bibliothèque Royale de Belgique* (Paris 1937), no. 54, pl. xxixd; Branner, 1971, 221, fig. 8; and Beer, 1972, figs. 13–14, 25–26, 28, 29b.
3. Purchased in 1946 by L. J. Rosenwald along with the National Gallery leaves.
4. See Branner, 1971, pp. 221ff.; Beer, 1972, pp. 191ff. Judging from the ratio of text to page, bifolio B would have comprised folios 3 and 6 of a quaternion.
5. Branner, 1971, pp. 221ff. See SISTER MINIATURES.
6. Those incipit miniatures extant (Genesis, Leviticus, Numbers, Joshua, and

Judges) all would have been part of volume 1. The first volume of such Bibles normally contained Genesis through Ruth. See Beer, 1972, p. 192f.

7. In addition, they all adopt the text of the Bible as revised in the course of the thirteenth century in Paris. See Beer, 1972, p. 191.

8. Ellen J. Beer, "Das Scriptorium des Johannes Philomena und seine Illuminatoren," *Scriptorium 23* (1969) [*Hommage à M. Frédéric Lyna*], pp. 24ff.; and Beer, 1972, passim.

9. Branner, 1971, 224, fig. 5; John Plummer, *The Glazier Collection of Illuminated Manuscripts* (New York: The Pierpont Morgan Library, 1968), no. 32, pl. 31.

10. Branner, 1971, p. 220; and Beer, 1972, p. 191, figs. 1–4.

11. See note 2.

12. Beer, 1972, passim (figs. 6–7, 9–10, 15, 17, 20, 22–24, 27, 29a).

13. Otto Pächt and J. J. G. Alexander, *Illuminated Manuscripts in the Bodleian Library, Oxford: 1, German, Dutch, Flemish, French and Spanish Schools* (Oxford 1966), no. 288, pl. xx; Beer, 1969, p. 36, pl. 11b.

14. Branner, 1971, p. 220; Beer, 1972, figs. 8, 29c.

Fig. 37f. *The Lord Speaks to Judah*. Philadelphia, Museum of Art, cod. 46.65.1 (detail)

38

Leaf from a Book of Hours
(or Psalter-Hours)

Crucifixion
Arras (?), c. 1290–1295
B-15,390
156 x 107   (6 1/8 x 4 1/4)

CONDITION   (G) Vellum soiled; vertical creases in left center; features of right nun retouched; colors slightly faded and rubbed; gold moderately flaked; trimmed top and bottom; penciled *17* in upper left (reverse: *18* with superimposed red *17*)

PROVENANCE   J. Rosenthal, Munich (1931); E. Rosenthal, Berkeley; L. J. Rosenwald, Jenkintown (1949); National Gallery of Art (1949)

EXHIBITED   Munich, 1931, no. 8

BIBLIOGRAPHY   Robert Branner, "A Cutting from a Thirteenth-Century French Bible," *The Bulletin of The Cleveland Museum of Art 58* (Sept. 1971), 227n

VERSO (?)   Blank

RECTO (?) (*fig. 38a; Colorplate* VIII)   Two Franciscan nuns (order of Poor Clares) kneel in adoration, each holding an extended banderole: (left) *Xp [Christ]e. tui. munda;* and (right) *[?]ve p[e]ccator[em] miserere.* The plaque on the cross carries the inscription: *Ih[e]s[us] Nazaren[us] Rex Iudeor[um]* (John 19:19).

This leaf was probably excised from a Book of Hours (or Psalter-Hours) where it typically would have served as one of a set of pictures illustrating the life of Christ at the beginning of the manuscript.[1] Stylistically, it stands at one remove from the innovations of the late thirteenth century, most elegantly employed by the Parisian workshop of Master Honoré. Although the illuminator of our miniature does not show the exactness and finesse of contemporary Parisian products his figure of Christ is comparable to that of a Crucifixion in a Missal and Breviary, intended for the church of Saint-Étienne in Châlons-sur-Marne, though probably produced in Paris around 1297 (Paris, Bibliothèque de l'Arsenal, cod. 595).[2] The restricted color scheme, frozen animation, and axial disposition evident in the Rosenwald miniature suggest an origin in northern France.[3]

More specifically, Alison Stones has associated the Rosenwald leaf with a workshop, most probably located in Arras, whose dated manuscripts fall between 1278 and 1310.[4] Especially similar is the leafy ornament of a manuscript now in the Bibliothèque Nationale, Paris (cod. franc. 350).[5] Since, according to Ms. Stones, the calendars of all other liturgical books from this atelier (with one exception) exclude Saint Louis, canonized in 1297, the production of the Rosenwald leaf should probably be dated no later than the early 1290s. The presence of kneeling donors, a new feature of this period (especially in Books of Hours),[6] suggests that the parent manuscript was commissioned by a convent of Franciscan nuns.

The Rosenwald Crucifixion includes an unusual iconographic detail. On the right a soldier holds aloft the crown of thorns instead of the sponge which would ordinarily be used as an iconographic and compositional counterpart to the lance on the left.[7] As a result of a purchase from the last Latin emperor of Constantinople, part of the true cross and the crown of thorns had come to Paris, shortly before 1240.[8] The crown of thorns, which was hailed as the most glorious relic in France, became a prominent feature in depictions of Christ's Passion in France and England, especially during the second half of the thirteenth century. While the Rosenwald miniature reflects that trend, it is quite unusual in showing the crown in the hands of a soldier (and not on the head of Christ).

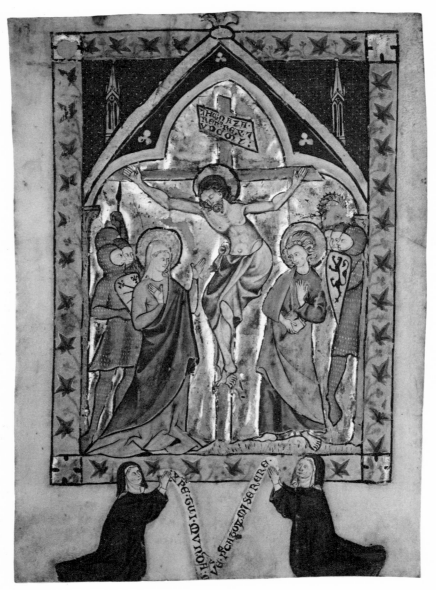

Fig. 38a. 1:1

1. The pagination *17* appearing on this leaf suggests that it was preceded by
a set of eight similar miniatures. M. Alison Stones, in a very informative letter
of June 26, 1974, points out that the format of contemporary Missals is con-
siderably larger. On the other hand, comparable full-page miniatures in Books
of Hours (and Psalter-Hours), although not common, are known from this period.
2. *Art and the Courts: France and England from 1259 to 1328* (Ottawa: National
Gallery of Canada, 1972), 2 vols., no. 8, pl. 11 (fol. 234v).
3. For a discussion of a number of northern French and English manuscripts
of the period, see Ottawa, 1972, esp. nos. 12–17 and Peter Brieger's introduction
("Manuscripts," vol. 1, pp. 50ff.).
4. See note 1. Robert Branner associated this leaf with late thirteenth-century
Arras in the 1971 article cited in the bibliography.
5. Compare especially its curious thorny leaves painted *without contours*.
6. Ottawa, 1972, p. 65.
7. We would like to thank Professor Rosalie Green for a very informative letter
regarding the iconography of this leaf (September 10, 1974). As Dr. Green points
out, the soldier holding the lance also supports a spongelike mass in his left
hand. This lump, however, is colored the same blue as the figure's armor.
8. The relics were installed at Sainte Chapelle by Louis IX. See Robert Branner,
St. Louis and the Court Style (London 1965), pp. 56ff.

39

Leaf from a Book of Hours

Saint Christopher carrying the Christ Child

Paris, c. 1409, "Atelier of the Limbourg Brothers"

B-13,520

206 x 149   (8 1/8 x 5 5/8)

Gothic minuscule script; 1 column of 19 lines (20?, top ruling unused) (130 [20 lines]–124 [19 lines] x 84 mm)

CONDITION   (G) Minor flaking and rubbing throughout; facial detail marred; lower left border ornament smeared; mold spots in lower half; several red stains along left side

PROVENANCE   J. Rosenthal, Munich (1931); E. Rosenthal, Berkeley; L. J. Rosenwald, Jenkintown (1946); National Gallery of Art (1946)

EXHIBITED   Munich, 1931, no. 20; Baltimore, 1949, no. 78; Los Angeles, 1953–1954, no. 51; *The International Style* (Baltimore: Walters Art Gallery, 1962), no. 56, illus.; *Pages from Medieval and Renaissance Illuminated Manuscripts from the Xth to the Early XVIth Centuries* (Berkeley: University Art Gallery, 1963), no. 38; Trenton, 1971, no. 32; illus.

BIBLIOGRAPHY   A. L. M., "Two Exhibitions at Munich," *The Burlington Magazine 59, no. 341* (Aug. 1931), 85; Millard Meiss, "The Exhibition of French Manuscripts of the XIII–XVI Centuries at the Bibliothèque Nationale," *The Art Bulletin 37, no. 3* (Sept. 1956), 195, fig. 10; Millard Meiss, *French Painting in the Time of Jean de Berry; the Limbourgs and their Contemporaries*, New York, 1974, p. 362.

RECTO *(fig. 39a)*   Christopher, patron saint of travelers, is dressed in a light beige cloak over a pale yellow-green tunic; the Christ Child on his shoulders wears blue. Toward the lower left a hermit, in an ample gray cloak, holds up a small gold lantern. The landscape shades from pale green in the foreground to earth tones in the middle distance, and gray-tan in the background. Likewise the water of the river and bay shades from white to gray, and the sky from deep blue to light blue at the horizon.

According to legend Saint Christopher was a mighty Canaanite (twelve cubits tall) who desired to serve the greatest of all kings. After rejecting an earthly king because he feared the devil, and the devil because he feared the cross, Christopher found a hermit who told him of Christ, and instructed him to ferry passengers across a large river as a means of service. After transporting, with great difficulty, the Christ Child across the river, Christopher was instructed to implant his staff on the shore, whereupon it miraculously bore fruit.

VERSO *(fig. 39b)*   Saint Christopher prayer: *Martir Xp [Christ] ofore pro salvatoris honore . . .* (to) . . . *congregatam pecudes meri* (?)

This miniature once formed part of a luxurious early fifteenth-century French Book of Hours where it served as frontispiece to the memorial of Saint Christopher (verso), within the Suffrages of the Saints. The massive head of Saint Christopher, as well as the intense features of the hermit, and the open, delicately modeled face of the Christ Child are details worthy of the Limbourg brothers.[1] Specifically, the hermit's physiognomy shows parallels to those of Saint Anthony and the Centaur in the *Belles Heures* of Jean, Duc de Berry (New York, The Metropolitan Museum of Art, The Cloisters, cod. 54. 1. 1),[2] dated by Millard Meiss to 1406–1408,[3] while the figure of Saint Christopher is a more grandiose version of its counterpart in the same manuscript.[4] On the other hand, the curiously out-of-scale rock formation on the right, the abrupt transition in the shading of the water, and the strange wheat-yellow trail ending at the hem of the hermit's robe suggest an assistant illuminator.

Fig. 39a. 1:1

The dating and original provenance of the Rosenwald leaf involves speculation. While its figure types and border ornament resemble the *Belles Heures*,[5] its deep landscape, greater monumentality, and full-page format recall the *Très Riches Heures* of Jean, Duc de Berry (Chantilly, Musée Condé, cod. 1284), a manuscript begun by the Limbourg brothers in 1413 and left unfinished at the death of its patron and all three brothers in 1416.[6] The Rosenwald leaf suggests the intriguing possibility that other fragments may yet be found from an untraced Book of Hours illuminated in the Limbourg atelier.[7]

1. In 1931, Friedrich Winkler attributed this leaf to Pol de Limbourg (Munich, 1931, no. 20). In 1956, Millard Meiss assigned it to the "atelier of the Limbourgs," a classification maintained in his 1974 monograph, in which he dates the leaf c. 1409 (see BIBLIOGRAPHY). We would like to thank Professor Meiss for generously communicating his judgment in advance of the appearance of his book.
2. James J. Rorimer and Margaret B. Freeman, *The Belles Heures of Jean, Duke of Berry Prince of France* (New York 1958), pl. 23, Meiss, pp. 102–141, fig. 479.
3. Millard Meiss, *French Painting in the Time of Jean de Berry: The Late XIV Century and the Patronage of the Duke* (London 1967, second ed. 1969), p. 92; Millard Meiss, "The Master of the Breviary of Jean Sans Peur and the Limbourgs," *Proceedings of the British Academy 56* (1970), 112.
4. Jean Porcher, *Les Belles Heures de Jean de France, Duc de Berry* (Paris 1953), pl. XCIX.
5. The Rosenwald borders are significantly more simple, both in the design of the framing bars and knots, and in the rinceaux and ivy leaf.
6. Jean Longnon, Raymond Cazelles, and Millard Meiss, *The Très Riches Heures of Jean, Duke of Berry* (New York 1969) [facsimile].
7. There are four text leaves from a Book of Hours in the Mark Lansburgh Collection, Colorado Springs, which are in dimensions (210 x 150 mm) script, proportion of text block to page, and border design remarkably close to the Rosenwald Leaf, as well as to the *Belles Heures*. See Mark Lansburgh, "The Illuminated Manuscript Collection at Colorado College," *Art Journal 27, no. 1* (Fall 1968), 64, fig. 6.

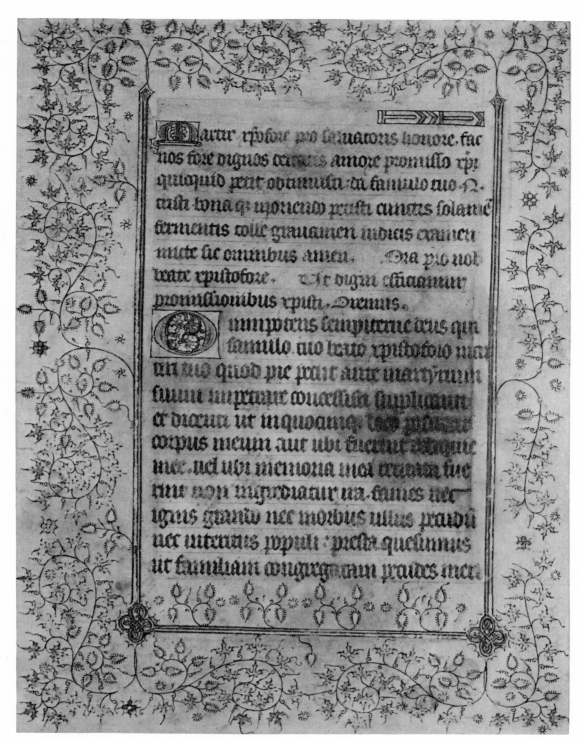

Fig. 39b. Verso, 1:1

40

Four Leaves from a Book of Hours

John (A); *Luke* (B);
Matthew (C); *Mark* (D)
Loire Region (?), c. 1425–1435
B-14,835 (A); B-14,836 (B);
B-14,838 (C); B-14,837 (D)
Average: 170 (180 with vellum
repair) x 129   (6 3/4–7 1/8 x
5 1/8)

Gothic minuscule script; 1 column of 14 lines (average: 86 x 54 mm)

CONDITION   (VG/E) Colors clear and fresh; gold tarnished and slightly flaked; minor rubbing (especially A); vellum translucent; all trimmed along top; all (but A) repaired with 10 mm vellum strip; B, verso: penciled *2* upper left; D, recto: penciled *4* upper right

PROVENANCE   E. Rosenthal, Berkeley; L. J. Rosenwald, Jenkintown (1948); National Gallery of Art (1948)

EXHIBITED   Los Angeles, 1953–1954, no. 62 (Mark only); Trenton, 1971, nos. 36, 38 (John, Matthew); South Bend, 1972, nos. 18–21, illus.

A, RECTO *(fig. 40a)*   John 1:1. John, dressed in a brown-lined blue mantle over a green undergarment, sits in a black upholstered chair before a large lectern. He leans forward to write his Gospel on a long scroll. To the lower left stands a light brown eagle, John's symbol, with an identifying banderole in his claws: *S[anctus]/ iohan[nes]*. A wooden canopy with blue lining and green curtain extends above the saint. A low green ledge separates the light brown floor from an orange and gold tesserated background.

All four leaves bear elaborate foliate borders. Major tendrils, which begin at the bottom of the page, are bright red and blue, with subsidiary forms in pale green, orange, and beige. Flowers, berries, and birds are scattered among the tendrils.

A, VERSO   John 1:1—John 1:8 (. . . *ille lux: sed*).

B, RECTO *(fig. 40b)*   Luke 1:26. Luke, also portrayed as a scribe, turns away from a lectern with open codex to sharpen a pen. He wears a pink robe, blue cowl, and black skull cap. His small wooden stall is light brown, the floor two shades of green, and the background a pattern of blue, orange, and gold. Beyond his desk, which carries a scroll with the word *Lucas*, is a calf, the Evangelist's symbol. On the ledge above is a vase of lilies, symbol of the Annunciation which is narrated in the Luke Gospel passage transcribed below.

B, VERSO   Luke 1:26—Luke 1:31 (. . . *et vocabis*).

C, RECTO *(fig. 40c)*   Matt. 2:1. Matthew, with light blue habit, orange cowl, and long, dark blue mantle sits before a large desk with lectern, writing his Gospel on a long scroll. Behind the desk, wearing pink robes and holding an ink well, is Matthew's symbol, an angel. The floor and walls of the small chamber are green; the vaulted roof brown, and the background orange and gold.

C, VERSO   Matt. 2:1—2:5 (. . . *scriptum est per*).

D, RECTO   Matt. 2:12 (*regionem suam . . .*); *Deo gratis;* (bottom of page) title to Mark.

D, VERSO *(fig. 40d)*   Mark 16:14 (. . . *et expro[bravit]*). Mark, wearing a blue-lined pink mantle over a light brown undergarment, sits beneath a pink canopy fringed in green. The bright orange and white wings of his symbolic brown lion stand out against a dark blue background. The floor as well as the flowered curtain at the back left are green. The lion's scroll bears the inscription: *S[anctus] Marc*.

These four single leaves were excised from an as yet untraced French Book of Hours, where they headed the four short Gospel lessons characteristically found near the very beginning of such a prayer book. Whereas their eclectic style suggests a dating to the late 1420s, direct parallels are scarce and many of the motifs employed are standard for the period. The first three miniatures reflect the most common architectural iconography found among early fifteenth-

Fig. 40a. Recto, A, 1:1

Fig. 40b. Recto, B, 1:1

century Evangelist portraits,[1] while the tesserated backgrounds, over-all spatial treatment, and layered draperies continue formulas established in the last decade of the fourteenth century. The primary innovative aspect of these leaves is the naturalistic decoration of the borders.

Certain mannerisms in handling suggest that the illuminators of the Rosenwald portraits may have been familiar at least with the later works of the Boucicaut atelier. The peculiar flat faces, whose open features, high foreheads, and pursed mouths are rendered with a minimum of shadow, recall the physiognomies in Books of Hours in the Bradfer-Lawrence Collection, Ripon,[2] and in the Library of Congress (cod. acc. 4560[7]).[3] Parallels also exist in the Evangelist portraits of a Book of Hours in a private New York collection.[4] The features shared with the above codices, all products of the last phases of the Boucicaut workshops, also appear in Boucicaut related workshops, especially that of the Bedford Master.

In conception and handling the portrait of Saint Mark is closest to the Boucicaut tradition, and stands somewhat apart from the other three portraits. Mark is more monumentally conceived, his drapery reflects more clearly the body beneath, and his head shows an intensity absent in his three clean-shaven counterparts. Furthermore, only his halo is rayed and only his miniature does not employ the tesserated background.

A particularly interesting aspect of our leaves is their borders, whose birds, insects, and various species of plant life are observed with considerable naturalism. The transformation of border decoration from the abstract ivy patterns of the style of Charles V to the marginal gardens of the third decade of the century, which appear in the work of the Bedford Master and the Master of the Hours of Marguerite d'Orléans, begins in the work of the Limbourgs.[5] Whether adopted from Flemish art or Italian models,[6] the tendency toward naturalism soon spread to the Boucicaut and other ateliers. Parallels for the Rosenwald borders may be traced among codices belonging to the group around the Master of the Hours of Marguerite d'Orléans. Much less lavish than her Book of Hours in Paris (Bibliothèque Nationale, cod. lat. 1156b),[7] our leaves show greater similarity to the Book of Hours in the Pierpont Morgan Library (cod. M157), and especially to the Book of Hours in the Biblioteca Trivulziana (cod. 2164).[8]

1. See Millard Meiss, "French and Italian Variations on an Early Fifteenth-Century Theme: St. Jerome and his Study," *Gazette des Beaux-Arts 62* (Sept. 1963), 147ff.
2. Millard Meiss, *French Painting in the Time of Jean de Berry: The Boucicaut Master* (New York 1968), p. 135, figs. 124, 249–250.
3. Meiss, 1968, p. 137, figs. 165, 296–298.
4. Meiss, 1968, 104f., figs. 133, 300–315 (esp. 300–301).
5. See Millard Meiss, "The Master of the Breviary of Jean Sans Peur and the Limbourgs," *Proceedings of the British Academy 56* (1970), esp. 125ff.
6. See Otto Pächt, "Early Italian Nature Studies and the Early Calendar Landscape," *Journal of the Warburg and Courtauld Institutes 13*, nos. 1–2 (Jan.–June 1950), 13ff.
7. Camille Couderc, *Les Enluminures des manuscrits du moyen age (du VIe au XVe siècle) de la Bibliothèque Nationale* (Paris 1927), pl. LVI.
8. Caterina Santoro, *I Codici miniati della Biblioteca Trivulziana* (Milan 1958), no. 116, pls. LXXXIX–XCIX.

Fig. 40c. Recto, C, 1:1

Fig. 40d. Verso, D, 1:1

41

Three Leaves from a Choir Book (Antiphonary)

David in Prayer (A) *Isaac Blessing Jacob* (B)
The Flagellation (C)
Bohemia (Prague), 1400–1405, close to the Master of the Golden Bull
B-18,755 (A); B-18,756 (B); B-18,753 (C)
All three: c. 559 x 402
(22 3/8 x 16)

Gothic minuscule script with four-line staff in red (32 mm); 7 lines, each accompanied by a staff (c. 405 x 280 mm)

CONDITION A   (VG/E) Details precise; only minor flaking; head of God slightly rubbed; small hole in center of leaf; foliated *51* (?) in upper right of recto

B   (VG/E) Colors, gold very fresh; Jacob's garment rubbed (tarnished?); diagonal crease (with minor flaking) across upper third of miniature; leaf trimmed along fore-edge; foliated *206* in upper right of recto

C   (E) Colors, facial detail very fresh and precise; gold to right of initial heavily rubbed; foliated *255* in upper right; penciled *4* in upper right

PROVENANCE   Up to early 1920s part of a Benedictine Antiphonary in the Austrian monastery of Seitenstetten; sold (with companion leaves) through Maggs Brothers of London in 1928; A: L. J. Rosenwald, Jenkintown (1950, through Sotheby); B, C: Rosenbach; L. J. Rosenwald, Jenkintown (1950); A, B, C: National Gallery of Art (1950)

EXHIBITED   Trenton, 1971, no. 31 (A)

BIBLIOGRAPHY   Maggs Brothers, *Music, Early Books, Manuscripts, Portraits and Autographs* [Sale Catalogue no. 512, 1928] (London 1928), lots. 297, 300, 302; Sotheby and Company, [Sale Catalogue, March 27, 1950] (London 1950); Gerhard Schmidt, "Fragmente eines böhmischen Antiphonariums des frühen 15. Jahrhunderts (ehemals in Seitenstetten) und eine Marientod-Initiale der Rosenwald Collection,"

Fig. 41d. Verso, A, detail, 1:1

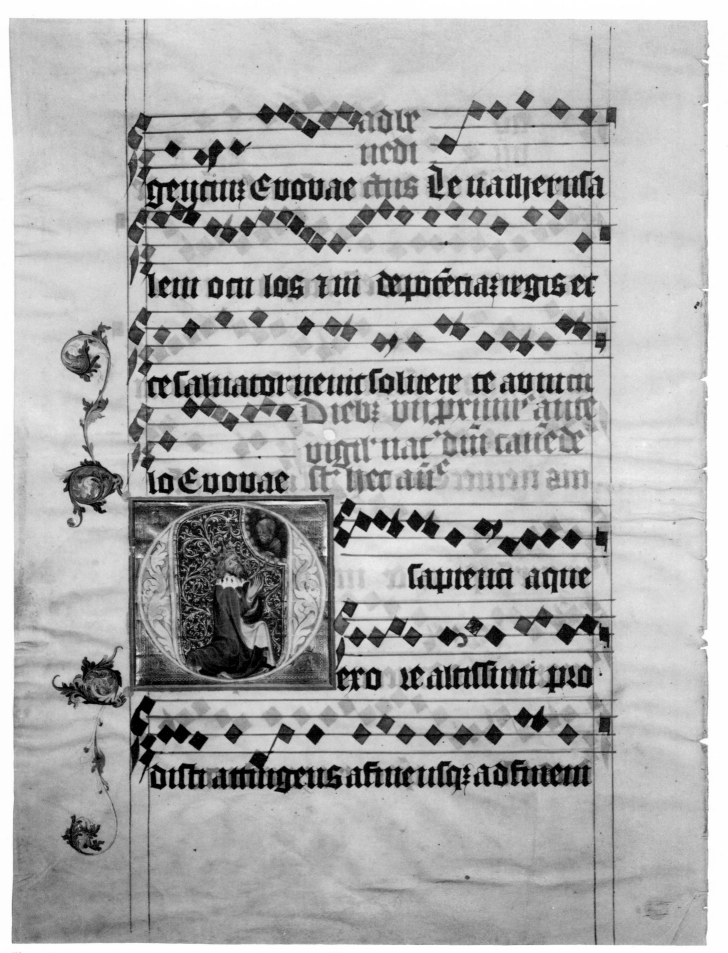

Fig. 41a

Fig. 41g. *The Nativity*. Montreal, L.V. Randall Collection (detail)

Wiener Jahrbuch für Kunstgeschichte 22 (1969), 148ff., figs. 193, 197, 207; Josef Krása (review of Schmidt) in *Umění 18, no. 4* (Oct. 1970), 413

PARENT MANUSCRIPT   Formerly: Seitenstetten, monastic library[1]

SISTER MINIATURES[2]

1) Location unknown (Maggs 289, pl. xxxi): single leaf with initial A; Christ Enthroned

2) [A (Maggs 300)]

3) Montreal, L. V. Randall Collection: single leaf with initial O; Nativity (*fig. 41g*)[3]

4) Location unknown (Maggs 293): single leaf with initial N; Saint Stephan

5) No longer extant (formerly: Vienna, Askonas Collection): single leaf with initial U; John the Evangelist[4]

6) Location unknown (Maggs 296): single leaf with initial O; Massacre of the Innocents

7) Location unknown (Maggs 291, pl. xxxiii): single leaf with initial M; Adoration of the Magi

8) [B (Maggs 302)]

9) Stockholm, National Museum, cod. N.M.B. 1714 (Maggs 294): single leaf with initial E; Stoning of Christ (*fig. 41h*)[5]

10) [C (Maggs 297)]

11) Location unknown (Maggs 296): single leaf with initial N; "the Magdalene consoled by Jesus"

12) Location unknown (Maggs 299): single leaf with initial D; Meeting of Abraham and Melchisedech

Fig. 41e. Verso, B, detail, 1:1

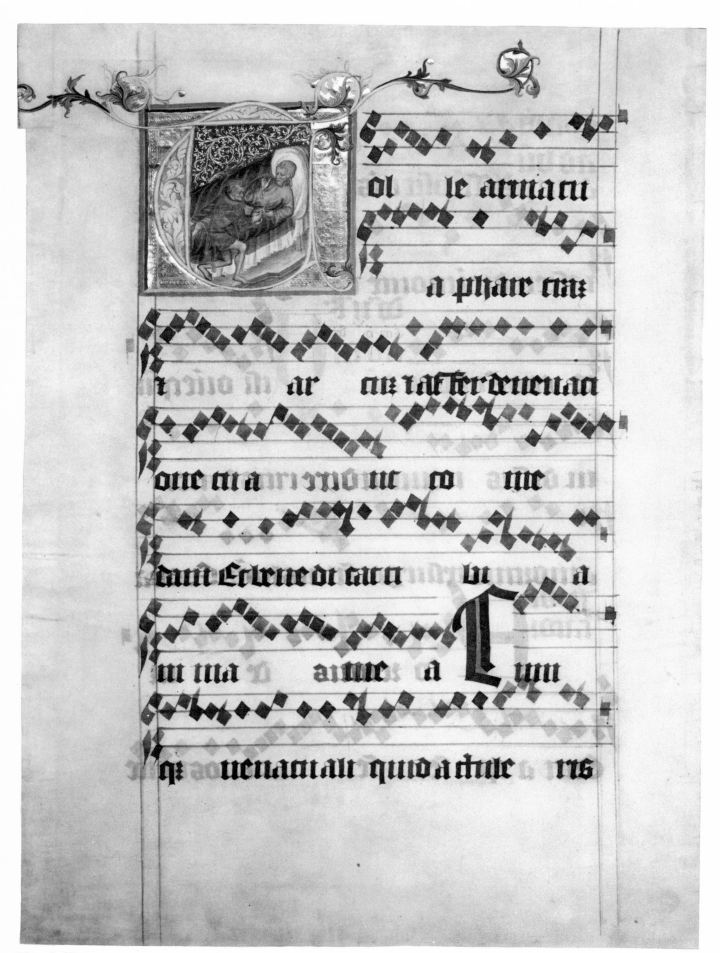

Fig. 41b. Verso, B

13) Location unknown (Maggs 303): single leaf with initial L; holy figure writing in a book

14) Location unknown (Maggs 305): single leaf with initial O: Noah's Ark.[6] *Note:* One more leaf from the same set very recently appeared for sale: Maggs Brothers, Limited, *European Miniatures and Illuminations* [Maggs Brothers, Ltd.: *Bulletin no. 8*, June, 1974] (London 1974), no. 13.

A, RECTO   Two antiphons for Saturday of the fourth week in Advent(?): *Dies Domini;* and *Non aufere.*

A, VERSO *(figs. 41a, 41d)*   Antiphon *ad benedictus* for Saturday of the fourth week in Advent(?): *Leva iherusalem;* followed by the beginning of the first of the antiphons for the week preceding Christmas (Dec. 17): *O Sapientia . . . (to) . . . ad finem.* (Eccles. 24:5: O Wisdom, who camest out of the mouth of the Most High. . . .)

King David, who wears a green robe lined in light red, kneels before God the Father, peering out from a small segment of blue. The light red acanthus of the initial encloses a grayish-blue field ornamented in gold. The framing gold square shows a finely incised vegetal pattern bounded by rows of quatrefoil punchwork.

B, RECTO   First antiphon for Saturday of the first week in Lent; *Assu[m]psit ih[esu]s disciplos;* followed by the invitatory to the second Sunday in Lent: *Adoremus deum quia ipse.*

B, VERSO *(figs. 41b, 41e;* Colorplate IX)   First response for the second Sunday in Lent: *Tolle arma tua* (Take thy weapons, thy quiver and thy bow, and bring your venison to me that I may eat; that my soul may bless thee); followed by a verse, up to: *. . . aliquid attuleris.*

This response is based on Gen. 27:3–4, the opening verses of the narrative which describes Jacob's deceitful scheme for obtaining the

Fig. 41f. Recto, c, detail, 1:1

156

Fig. 41c. Recto, c

blessing of his father Isaac which was due his brother Esau (Gen.
27:1–29). Isaac, his eyes nearly shut with age, raises his left hand in a
gesture of blessing while touching a small gray rabbit used by Jacob
to approximate the hairy quality of Esau's hands (according to Gen.
27:16, Jacob used "the skins of the kids").

C, RECTO (*figs. 41c, 41f*)   Response for the Saturday before Palm
Sunday: *Circumdederunt me viri mendaces sine causa flagellis
ceciderunt me sed tu domine defensor vindica [mea].*

Christ, bound to a mauve column, is tormented from the left by a
figure in gray, and from the right by a figure in maroon brown.
The background of this initial is scarlet, its square frame is (untooled)
gold, and its foliate extenders pink, green, and blue, with gold filler.

C, VERSO   Conclusion of the response from the recto; followed by a
verse: *Duo viam;* an antiphon: *Clarifica me;* and the invitatory for
Palm Sunday: *Ipsi vero non . . .* (to) *. . . vias mie.*

These three leaves are among at least fourteen thus far identified by
Gerhard Schmidt as having formed part of a Benedictine Antiphonary,
intact in the Austrian monastery of Seitenstetten until shortly after

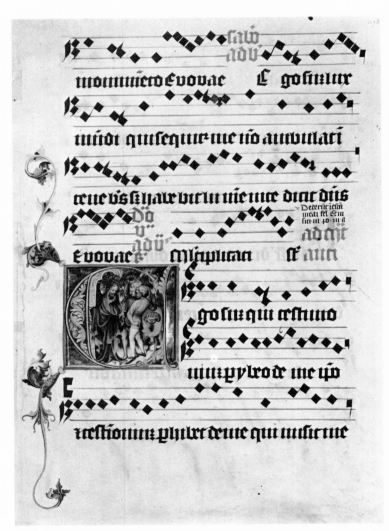

Fig. 41h. *Stoning of Christ.* Stockholm, National Museum, cod. N.M.B.1714

World War I.[7] Stylistically, they may be assigned to early fifteenth-century Prague on the basis of very close parallels of drapery, head type, and landscape treatment with miniatures in the *Golden Bull* (Vienna, Nationalbibliothek, cod. 338), produced in that city in 1400 for King Wenceslaus IV.[8] Also quite similar are the drapery style, facial types, and border ornament of the more advanced of the illuminators responsible for the Missal of Wenceslaus of Radeč (Prague, Kapitelbibl., cod. P. 5), also executed in Prague around 1400.[9]

While Professor Schmidt emphasizes the importance of the above parallels, he nonetheless is reluctant to identify the leading artistic personality of the Seitenstetten Antiphonary with either of those masters, preferring instead an independent, "eclectic" master.[10] Moreover, he suggests a date near the middle of the decade on the basis of parallels in the Nativity iconography, and zoomorphic border motifs of the Hasenburg Missal of 1409 (Vienna, National-bibliothek, cod. 1844);[11] and a general correspondence of stylistic level with several illuminators active in the Bible of Konrad of Vecta (Antwerp, Musée Plantin-Moretus, cod. 15.1–2), dated 1403.[12]

Although Schmidt raises the possibility that the larger initials (three lines high as opposed to the two-line Rosenwald miniatures) represent the work of a second, superior illuminator, the consistent repetition of initial format, gold tooling,[13] and border vegetal motifs indicate an origin for all known miniatures in one atelier.

1. Schmidt, 1969, 155f. The codex was sold and dismembered soon after World War I.
2. This list is based on that given in Gerhard Schmidt's 1969 article (p. 155; see BIBLIOGRAPHY). Leaves 1 to 10 are in their original sequence as determined by Dr. Schmidt on the basis of liturgical order and foliation. Leaves 1–2, 4, 6–14 were sold through Maggs Brothers in 1928 (see BIBLIOGRAPHY). Each measures c. 560–570 x 400–405 mm.
3. Schmidt, 1969, p. 149, fig. 195.
4. Schmidt, 1969, p. 149, fig. 194.
5. Schmidt, 1969, fig. 205.
6. A very closely related leaf was sold through Sotheby in 1962, showing Christ with a suppliant in an initial D (555 x 380 mm). See Sotheby and Company, *Important Old Master Drawings* [Sale Catalogue: June 28, 1962] (London 1962), lot. 46, illus.; Schmidt, 1969, 149, 155. As Schmidt points out, the leaf carries the gathering number XVI which would make it approximately the 128th folio. On the other hand, its text *(Domine ne in ira tua arguas me)* is a response introducing the Penetential Psalms which would not be found before the Epiphany leaf (no. 7 above), which bears the folio number 191. Also, the suppliant is not a monk.
7. See SISTER MINIATURES and note 2.
8. See Alfred Stange, *Deutsche Malerei der Gotik 2: 1350–1400* (reprint: Nendeln/Liechtenstein, 1969), figs. 48–49; Schmidt, 1969, p. 150f., figs. 200, 208. The association with the Master of the Golden Bull was proposed by Otto Pächt in the 1962 sale catalogue entry for the closely related leaf discussed in note 6. Recently Dr. Pächt has also ascribed the three Rosenwald initials to the Golden Bull master.
9. Schmidt, 1969, p. 150f., figs. 192, 199. Jaroslav Pesina assigned the now-lost Askonas leaf (no. 5 in list) to the illuminator of the Missal of Wenceslaus of Radeč in 1960. See Jaroslav Pešina, "Novy pokus o revizi dějin Českého malířství 15 století," *Umění 8* (1960), 109ff.
10. Schmidt, 1969, p. 151.
11. Schmidt, 1969, p. 151, fig. p. 196.
12. Especially the so-called "Noah Master" responsible for gatherings 2, 7, and 10. See Schmidt, 1969, p. 152, fig. 198.
13. Neither the Rosenwald Flagellation nor the Stockholm Stoning of Christ show any gold tooling. Since both originated at points well into the codex (fols. 243, 255) it is likely that they were never finished. The Rosenwald figure of Christ does not even show a cruciform halo.

42

Initial G from a Choir Book (Gradual)

Christ and the Virgin Enthroned
Bohemia (?), c. 1410–1420
B-22,895
137 x 118   (5 3/8 x 4 11/16)

Gothic minuscule script with five-line staff in red (29 mm)

CONDITION   (VG) Colors and detail within initial very well preserved; gold and parts of green frame show stains and flaking; pentimenti visible within initial structure

PROVENANCE   L. J. Rosenwald, Jenkintown (1962, through L'Art Ancien); National Gallery of Art (1962)

EXHIBITED   Trenton, 1971, no. 23; South Bend, 1972, no. 14

RECTO *(fig. 42a)*   Beginning of the Introit for the Feast of the Assumption of the Virgin (Aug. 15): G[*audeamus omnes*]. (Let us all rejoice in the Lord, celebrating a feast in honor of the Blessed Virgin Mary. . . .)

Christ, holding a small gold globe (symbolizing His imperial role), is dressed in two shades of light orange; the Virgin's garments are light blue lined with green. Both figures wear large jeweled crowns. The bluish-gray initial encloses a field of dark reddish brown, delicately ornamented in gold, and is in turn set against a gold rectangle framed in light green.

VERSO *(fig. 42b)*   Continuation of the Introit from the recto: *dei. E*[*ructavit cor*] *meum verbum bo*[*num: dico eg*]*o opera mea regi.*

This initial, which was formerly part of a large illuminated choir book where it marked the Feast of the Assumption of the Virgin, shows stylistic parallels with miniatures and panel paintings produced during the first two decades of the fifteenth century in Bohemia and in neighboring areas under Bohemian influence. For example, the facial type of Christ; His brittle fingers; unusual proportions (large head and narrow, sloping shoulders); rhythmic, voluminous drapery (with its nervous hemline); and the miniature's dark, ornamented background, all have counterparts among those miniatures of the 1403 Bible of Konrad of Vecta (Antwerp, Musée Plantin-Moretus, cod. 15. 1–2), executed by the so-called Gerona Master.[1]

An attribution to that or any other workshop is difficult, however, since this mannered drapery style as well as the facial types and the general initial format are characteristic of the period. A closely comparable initial structure and correspondingly full drapery style appear in an Austrian Antiphonary datable to the early 1420s (Klosterneuburg, cod. 67),[2] while the facial type of the Virgin (large, high forehead; receding, fleshy chin with full lips; and long blond hair) is paralleled by that of Saint Catherine in a small panel (vellum on wood) in Innsbruck (Museum Ferdinandeum), dated by Gerhard Schmidt to c. 1415–1420.[3]

Recently Professor Gerhard Schmidt has postulated a dating for the Rosenwald initial in the second decade of the century, suggesting that its illuminator was familiar with the mature works of the Master of the Golden Bull and above-cited workshop employed on the Vecta Bible.[4]

Fig. 42b. Verso

1. This is Vermeiren's "third workshop." Marie-Louise Vermeiren, "La Bible de Wenceslas du Musée Plantin-Moretus à Anvers," *De Gulden Passer 31, nos. 3, 4* (1953), 206, figs. 214–215, 222. Similarities are most evident in the unfinished miniatures. See Mojmír Frinta, "The Master of the Gerona Martyrology and Bohemian Illumination," *The Art Bulletin 46, no. 3* (Sept. 1964), 282ff., figs. 1, 9.
2. Gerhard Schmidt, "Die Buchmalerei;" *Die Gotik in Niederösterreich*, eds. Fritz Dworschak and Harry Kühnel (Vienna 1963), pl. 42a. In a letter of

Fig. 42a. 1:1

August 14, 1974, Professor Mojmír Frinta suggested an Austrian localization for this fragment, pointing out that while its drapery style shows parallels with Bohemian products, the facial type of the Virgin does not.

3. Gerhard Schmidt, "Malerei bis 1450: Tafelmalerei-Wandmalerei-Buchmalerei," *Gotik in Böhmen*, ed. Karl Swoboda (Munich 1969), pl. 198.

4. We would like to thank Professor Schmidt for sharing his opinion of this fragment with us. For the Master of the Golden Bull, see Alfred Stange, *Deutsche Malerei der Gotik 2: 1350–1400* (reprint: Nendeln/Liechtenstein, 1969), figs. 48–49; and Schmidt, 1969, pp. 150f., figs. 200, 208.

43

Initial G from a Choir Book
(Gradual)

Death of the Virgin
Bohemia (Prague), c. 1410,
"Joshua Master" (?)
B-18,752
162 x 168   (6 3/8 x 6 5/8)

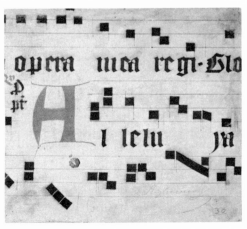

Fig. 43b. Verso

Gothic minuscule script with four-line staff in black (30 mm)

CONDITION   (VG) Colors and detail very fresh; several (deep) horizontal wrinkles have caused only minor flaking

PROVENANCE   E. Rosenthal, Berkeley; L. J. Rosenwald, Jenkintown (1951); National Gallery of Art (1951)

EXHIBITED   South Bend, 1972, no. 13, illus.

BIBLIOGRAPHY   Gerhard Schmidt, "Fragmente eines böhmischen Antiphonariums des frühen 15. Jahrhunderts (ehemals in Seitenstetten) und eine Marientod—Initiale der Rosenwald Collection," *Wiener Jahrbuch für Kunstgeschichte 22* (1969), 153f., fig. 202; Gerhard Schmidt, "Malerei bis 1450: Tafelmalerei-Wandmalerei-Buchmalerei," *Gotik in Böhmen*, ed. Karl Swoboda (Munich 1969), p. 254

RECTO *(fig. 43a)*   Beginning of the Introit for the Feast of the Assumption of the Virgin (Aug. 15): G[*audeamus omnes*]. (Let us all rejoice in the Lord, celebrating a feast in honor of the blessed Virgin Mary. . . .)

The Virgin, lying on a light grayish-yellow bed, is wrapped in a blue mantle lined in orange. The Apostles wear garments of yellowish green, gray, pale burgundy, yellowish orange, and blue. Only Paul, Peter, and John are identifiable by facial type (left to right behind the head of the Virgin). The background is a thin reddish brown covered with a fine gold arabesque. Christ, at the top center, is set against a deep red field enclosed by dark blue clouds; He holds the Virgin's soul on his left arm. The initial is rendered in shades of burgundy and is set against a gold ground. The border is bright yellowish green.

VERSO *(fig. 43b)*   End of the Introit from the recto: *Opera mea Regi. Glo*[*ria*] . . . *Alleluia.*

This colorful historiated initial was excised from an as yet untraced Bohemian choir book, where it marked the beginning of the mass celebrated on August 15th, the Feast of the Assumption of the Virgin. Professor Gerhard Schmidt has pointed out striking stylistic and technical similarities (punching patterns in the gold ground) between the Rosenwald cutting and the Resurrection initial (fol. 128v) in a Dominican Gradual in Prague (University Archives).[1] Further, he accepts J. Krása's attribution of the latter miniature to the late style of the so-called Joshua Master, who is first identifiable with the Joshua initial in the 1403 Bible of Konrad of Vecta (Antwerp, Musée Plantin-Moretus, cod. 15. 1–2, fol. 123v),[2] and dates both miniatures to around 1410. An attribution to the Joshua Master is further supported by parallels of style and figure type between the Rosenwald miniature and the center of the title page miniature of "the Host Mill" of a Bohemian Antiphonary in Lucerne (Cantonal Library, cod. PMS. 19, fol. 1r).[3] Both Jaroslav Pešina[4] and J. Krása[5] have identified the Lucerne "Host Mill" as a late miniature by the Joshua Master, the latter scholar dating it to around 1410.

Citing the artistic superiority of the Prague Ascension, Schmidt suggests that the Rosenwald miniature may actually have been executed by a workshop assistant to the Joshua Master. The question of collaboration is left unresolved, however, since the Lucerne miniature is itself not homogeneous: the Apostles within the initial closely parallel the Rosenwald Apostles, while the four corner prophet figures are linked with the Prague Ascension.[6]

Fig. 43a. 1:1

1. Schmidt, 1969 ("Fragmente . . ."), p. 153, fig. 203. See Josef Krása, "Na okraj nové studie a Mistu geronského Martyrologia," *Umení 14* (1966), fig. 3.
2. Krása, 1966, pp. 394ff. See Marie-Louise Vermeiren, "La Bible de Wenceslas du Musée Plantin-Moretus à Anvers," *De Gulden Passer 31, nos. 3, 4* (1953), 206, illus. opposite p. 198.
3. Joseph Schmid, *Les Plus belles miniatures de la Bibliothèque Cantonale de Lucerne* (Lucerne 1941), I, pl. 35.
4. Jaroslav Pešina, "Navý pokus o revizi dějin českého malířství 15. století," *Umění 8* (1960), 119.
5. Krása, 1966, 394ff. Dr. Mojmír Frinta has attributed "the Host Mill" to Master A active within the atelier of the so-called Master of the Gerona Martyrology, who also illuminated folios 113–127 of the Bible of Konrad of Vecta. See Mojmír Frinta, "The Master of the Gerona Martyrology and Bohemian Illumination," *The Art Bulletin 46, no. 3* (Sept. 1964), 289f., 294.
6. Schmidt, 1969 ("Fragmente . . ."), p. 154.

44

Initial V from a Choir Book
(Antiphonary)

The Trinity
Bohemia (Prague), 1414,
Workshop of the Gerona
Martyrology
B-13,512
157 x 182   (6 1/4 x 7 1/8)

Fig. 44b. Recto

Gothic minuscule script; 9 lines (incomplete) (rule: 17 mm)

CONDITION   (E) Colors and detail extremely fresh; gold, and Christ's cloak, show only minor rubbing (verso: E. Schultze stamp—Lugt no. 906, and R. Forrer stamp—Lugt suppl. 941a)

PROVENANCE   Cistercian monastery of Sedlec (near Kutná Hora); during the Hussite revolt it belonged to Abbot Oswald of the Austrian cloister at Lilienfeld; repurchased by Clement, Abbot of Sedlec in 1506; (probably) transferred to the Premonstratensian monastery at Nová Ríse with the dissolution of the Sedlec monastery in 1799;[1] E. Schultze; R. Forrer, Strasbourg; J. Rosenthal, Munich (1931); E. Rosenthal, Berkeley; L. J. Rosenwald, Jenkintown (1946); National Gallery of Art (1946)

EXHIBITED   Munich, 1931, no. 21; Baltimore, 1949, no. 141, illus.; National Gallery, 1950, no. 11, illus.; Los Angeles, 1953–1954, no. 89; *The International Style* (Baltimore: Walters Art Gallery, 1962), no. 66, illus.; *Europäische Kunst um 1400* (Vienna: Kunsthistorisches Museum, 1962), no. 184; *Pages from Medieval and Renaissance Illuminated Manuscripts from the xth to the Early xvith Centuries* (Berkeley: University Art Gallery, 1963), no. 31, illus.

BIBLIOGRAPHY   Mojmír S. Frinta, "The Master of the Gerona Martyrology and Bohemian Illumination," *The Art Bulletin 46, no. 3* (Sept. 1964), 293f., fig. 29; Zoroslava Drobná, "Quelques remarques sur l'antiphonaire de Sedlec de 1414," *Sborník prací fil. fak. Brněnské University 17* (1968), 39ff.; Gerhard Schmidt, "Malerei bis 1450: Tafelmalerei-Wandmalerei-Buchmalerei," *Gotik in Böhmen*, ed. Karl Swoboda (Munich 1969), p. 254

PARENT MANUSCRIPT   Brno, Staatsbibliothek, cod. NŘ 25:172 folios (575 x 398 mm); folio 172r: scribal colophon dated 1414 *(fig. 44c)*[2]

SISTER MINIATURES   All are in Budapest, The Museum of Fine Arts;
1) cod. 3110: single miniature (154 x 159 mm); the Entry into Jerusalem *(fig. 44d)*[3]
2) cod. 3111: single initial A (155 x 162 mm); the Three Holy Women at the Tomb *(fig. 44e)*[4]
3) cod. 3109: single initial D (162 x 160 mm); Pentecost *(fig. 44f)*[5]
4) cod. 3107: single initial S (151 x 157 mm); Pentecost *(fig. 44g)*[6]
5) cod. 3112: single miniature (155 x 162); Saint Benedict Giving his Rule *(fig. 44h)*[7]
There are three additional miniatures in the Budapest Museum of Fine Arts that are very closely related to the above group. While Z. Drobná considered all eight to be cut from the Sedlec Antiphonary (see note 1), M. Aggházy has suggested that the following three were cut from a Gradual:[8]
6) cod. 3105: single initial G (94 x 103 mm); Death of the Virgin[9]
7) cod. 3106: single initial V (152 x 158 mm); the Ascension *(fig. 44i)*[10]
8) cod. 3108: single initial T (149 x 142 mm); Jacob's Dream *(fig. 44j)*[11]

RECTO *(fig. 44b)*   9 lines of an as yet unidentified text

VERSO *(fig. 44a)*   (?) Beginning of an antiphon within nocturns for the Feast of the Holy Trinity (first Sunday after Pentecost): V [*erax est Pater veritas Filius.*]

God the Father is seated with both hands on a diminutive figure of Christ, who in turn holds His cross, surmounted by the Dove of the Holy Spirit. He is dressed in a long mantle of dark blue, highlighted in yellow-brown, while Christ wears a blue garment. The bright yellowish-green initial encloses a pale burgundy field with finely drawn gold decoration. It, in turn, is placed against a tooled gold ground framed in two shades of blue.

Fig. 44a. 1:1

165

Fig. 44c. *Saints Philip and James.* Brno, Staatsbibliothek, cod. NR25

Fig. 44d. *Entry into Jerusalem.* Budapest, Museum of Fine Arts, cod. 3110

Fig. 44e. *The Three Holy Women at the Tomb.* Budapest, Museum of Fine Arts, cod. 3111

This initial very probably marked the beginning of an antiphon to be sung during Divine Offices for the Feast of the Holy Trinity (first Sunday after Pentecost). More than ten years ago Professor Mojmír Frinta identified this fragment as part of a group with several choir book miniatures in The Museum of Fine Arts, Budapest, all cut from a Bohemian Antiphonary produced in 1414 for the Cistercian monastery of Sedlec (near Kutná Hora). On folio 172 recto of that codex is entered the following scribal note:

> *Hunc librum comparavit venerabilis in Christo pater et dominus, dominus Jacobus divina providentia Abbas Czedliczensis qui finitus est sexta feria in vigilia epiphanie sub anno domini milesimo* cccc°xiii°[12]

Dr. Frinta associated these twelve initials with the atelier which produced the Gerona Martyrology (Gerona, Diocesan Museum), and identified the participation of three illuminators.[13] He has suggested that (at least) the heads in the Rosenwald Trinity may be by "Master B" of the Gerona codex, who also did the Ascension, Pentecost II, probably Jacob's Dream, and the heads in the miniature of Saints Philip and James.[14] The style of the Gerona Master's work-shop is traced from its beginnings in the Genesis pages of the Korszek Bible (Vienna, Nationalbibliothek, cod. 1169, fols. 1r, 3v, 4r), dated by colophon to 1400,[15] through its development in the Bible of Konrad of Vecta (Antwerp, Musée Plantin-Moretus, cod. 15. 1–2), dated 1403,[16] and finally to its full flowering in the Gerona Martyrology,[17] the Sedlec Antiphonary and related monuments of the 1410s.

The iconography of the Rosenwald Trinity is unusual. The more standard formula, seen in a Bohemian initial G in The Cleveland Museum of Art (cod. 49.537),[18] shows Christ crucified on the cross. During the fourteenth century another type became prominent (exemplified by Jean Malouel's *Trinity with the Man of Sorrows* in the Louvre), wherein God supports the dead figure of Christ over whose head floats the Dove of the Holy Spirit. The Rosenwald miniature, less hieratic than the former type, shares the humanizing spirit of the fourteenth-century variation. God the Father, resigned to the fate of His Son, places his hand on Christ's shoulder as the latter accepts the cross. For the members of the monastic community of Sedlec who used this Antiphonary, a parallel must have existed between Christ's learning to take up the cross and the monk's learning *imitatio Christi.*

1. Zoroslava Drobná, 'Les Huit miniatures Tchèques de Budapest," *Bulletin du Musée National Hongrois des Beaux-Arts 11* (1957), 36.
2. A. Matějčk, "Sedlecký antifonár z roku 1414 v knihovně kláštera v Nové Ríši," *Památky Archeologické 34* (1924–1925), 216ff., pls. 99–101; Drobná, 1957, esp. 36ff., figs. 11, 13, 17–18. The manuscript still contains three figurative initials.
3. Drobná, 1957, pp. 32ff., fig. 20.
4. Drobná, 1957, p. 34, fig. 14.
5. Drobná, 1957, p. 32, fig. 15.
6. Drobná, 1957, p. 31f.; Frinta, 1964, fig. 26.
7. Drobná, 1957, p. 34; Frinta, 1964, fig. 24.
8. Maria Aggházy, "Remarques sur la question des 'Huit miniatures Tchèques de Budapest'," *Bulletin du Musée National Hongrois des Beaux-Arts 12* (1958), 46.
9. Drobná, 1957, p. 30.
10. Drobná, 1957, p. 30, fig. 12.
11. Drobná, 1957, p. 32, fig. 16.
12. Drobná, 1957, p. 36.

Fig. 44f. *Pentecost*. Budapest, Museum of Fine Arts, cod. 3109

13. Frinta, 1964, p. 292ff.

14. SISTER MINIATURES nos. 4, 7–8. The miniature of Saints Philip and James has not been excised from its parent manuscript. See Frinta, 1964, fig. 30. Dr. Frinta suggested discrepancies between the quality of the heads and the bodies in the Rosenwald miniature, assigning the latter to a lesser member of the atelier ("Master C"). The homogeneity of modeling, color, and handling, however, argues against such a distinction.

15. Frinta, 1964, pp. 298f., figs. 37–38.

16. Frinta, 1964, pp. 283ff.

17. Frinta, 1964, pp. 289ff. The work of Master B is scattered throughout the last third of the manuscript (see Frinta, 1964, pp. 291ff., figs. 18–20).

18. *Gothic Art 1360–1440* (Cleveland: The Cleveland Museum of Art, 1963), no. 1, illus.

Fig. 44g. *Pentecost*. Budapest, Museum of Fine Arts, cod. 3107

Fig. 44i. *The Ascension*. Budapest, Museum of Fine Arts, cod. 3106

Fig. 44h. *Saint Benedict Giving His Rule.* Budapest, Museum of Fine Arts, cod. 3112

Fig. 44j. *Jacob's Dream*. Budapest, Museum of Fine Arts, cod. 3108

45

Leaf from a Missal

Crucifixion
Lower Austria, Southern
Bohemia, c. 1430
B-15,386
202 X 153 (7 15/16 x 6 1/16)

Fig. 45b. Recto

Late Gothic minuscule script; 1 column of 28 (?) lines (26 standard lines used) (141 x 92 mm; ruled in brown)

CONDITION (VG) Very thin vellum has wrinkled; right side of frame soiled; pentimenti visible below the feet of the Virgin; five horizontal slits along right side from later re-binding

PROVENANCE E. Rosenthal, Berkeley; L. J. Rosenwald, Jenkintown (1949); National Gallery of Art (1949)

EXHIBITED National Gallery, 1950, no. 10; Trenton, 1971, no. 27

RECTO *(fig. 45b)* Continuation of prayers preceding the Canon: *michi aut[em] in digno . . . ; Orate fratres . . . ; Oblatus . . . secula seculorum. Amen;* [in red] *sequitur Canon Maior.*

VERSO *(fig. 45a)* The Virgin, whose veil is stained with several drops of blood, is dressed in a blue mantle over a light purple tunic. John's undergarment is the same color; his mantle is yellow-green, lined in beige. Streams of bright red blood fall from Christ's greenish-yellow body. The miniature's bright green frame encloses a dark purple-brown background. Above the knotted *tau* cross is a plaque with the inscription: *I[esus] N[azarenus] R[ex] I[udaeorum]* (John 19:19).

This single leaf originally formed part of a Missal, where its Crucifixion miniature would have served as frontispiece to that section containing the Canon of the Mass. While stylistically it shows affinities with fifteenth-century Bohemian and lower Austrian illumination, it lacks the decorative color scheme, elegant figures, and full, rhythmic drapery characteristic of products from the first and early second decades, such as the Crucifixion miniature in the Missal of Sbinko von Hasenburg (Vienna, Nationalbibliothek, cod. 1844).[1] Its harsh, realistic treatment should be compared instead with products from the period of the Hussite Wars (1419–1436)[2] and with the Rajhrad Altar (produced between 1415 and 1420), out of whose atelier much of that painting developed.[3] Iconographically the Rosenwald miniature shows close parallels to two later relatives of the Rajhrad Crucifixion panel:[4] the so-called Reinighaus Altar (early 1420s), and its iconographic duplicate, the Ottau Altar (mid-1430s), both in the National Gallery, Prague.[5] Recently, Gerhard Schmidt has suggested a relationship with the earliest works by the Viennese "Albrecht illuminator," although not an attribution to the hand of that artist himself.[6]

The Rosenwald miniature includes the peculiar iconographic detail of blood stains on the veil of the Virgin. Although not described in the Gospel accounts of the Crucifixion, such a motif is not uncommon in miniatures and panels of the early fifteenth century from Bohemia, South Germany, and Austria. Generally, it implies a parallel between Christ's suffering and that of the Virgin, and reflects the profound meditations on the Crucifixion by Heinrich Suso.[7]

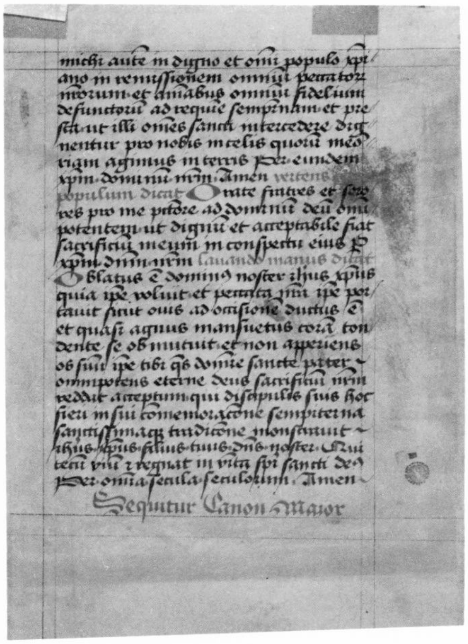

1. *Gotik in Böhmen*, ed. Karl Swoboda (Munich 1969), fig. 186.
2. P. Kropáček, *Malířství doby husitské* (Prague 1946), passim. See Gerhard Schmidt, "Malerei bis 1450: Tafelmalerei-Wandmalerei-Buchmalerei," *Gotik in Böhmen*, ed. Karl Swoboda (Munich 1969), pp. 318ff.
3. Schmidt, 1969, 319. See Antonín Matějček and Jaroslav Pešina, *Czech Gothic Painting* (Prague 1950), pp. 66ff. pls. 181–192. For example, the facial types and drapery style of the Rosenwald leaf are analogous to those in the *Christ*

Fig. 45a. 1:1

Carrying the Cross panel from that altar (Brno, Museum van Moravië, no. A 626) [see Matejcek and Pesina, 1950, pls. 181–183].

4. Prague, National Gallery, no. o 1584. See Maťejček and Pešina, 1950, pls. 184–186.

5. For the Reinighaus Altar see Matějček and Pešina, 1950, pl. 208. For the Ottau Altar see Matějček and Pešina, 1950, 74, pls. 222–225. These two panels reproduce *exactly* the Rosenwald figure of Christ on the Cross, while at the same time showing comparable drapery motifs, facial types, and brittle, arthritic hands. For Gerhard Schmidt's discussion of these two panels as representative of the transformation of Crucifixion iconography during the "Hussite period," see Schmidt, 1969, 319.

6. Thanks are due to Professor Schmidt for generously sharing his opinion of this leaf in a letter of August 14, 1974. The Albrecht illuminator is named from a large altarpiece now in the Stiftsmuseum of Klosterneuburg, apparently commissioned by Queen Elizabeth shortly after the death of her husband, Albrecht II, in 1439. See Ludwig Baldass, "Die Tafelmalerei," *Die Gotik in Niederösterreich*, ed. Fritz Dworschak and Harry Kühnel (Vienna 1963), p. 85, pls. 17, 20–21.

7. See Emile Mâle, *L'Art religieux de la fin du moyen age en France* (Paris 1931), pp. 85ff.; and Erwin Panofsky, *Early Netherlandish Painting* (Cambridge, Mass. 1953), p. 51.

46

Thirteen Initials from a Choir Book (Antiphonary)

Seville, 1430s, Master of the Cypresses (Pedro da Toledo?)

Four-line staff in red (74 mm)

PROVENANCE   W. Sterling, 1849 (penciled notation inside cover of former binding: "I bought these [14] cuttings [for the other cutting see cat. 49] from a Spanish '*Libros Deloro*' at Madrid in 1849. W. S."); B. Rosenthal, New York; L. J. Rosenwald, Jenkintown (1960); National Gallery of Art (1964)

EXHIBITED   Trenton, 1971, nos. 28-29, illus.; South Bend, 1972, nos. 24-31, illus.

These eight figurative and five purely ornamental initials were purchased as a group from a Spanish book dealer in the mid nineteenth century. Stylistically they show an amalgamation of Italian and Flemish influences and are closely tied to a group of approximately eighty historiated initials isolated by Angulo Iñiguez within a series of twenty choir books in the Cathedral of Seville.[1] The entire group, constituting the earliest and most distinct flowering of Seville choir book illumination, may be roughly assigned to the 1430s on the basis of close stylistic similarities to a series of frescoes in San Isidoro del Compo in Santiponce (especially the Last Supper in the refectory), datable between 1431–1436.[2] Iñiguez named the illuminator responsible for the Seville initials "the Master of the Cypresses" since large cypress trees are prominent features of many of his miniatures. Further, he presented evidence to identify this master with a certain Pedro da Toledo, who, according to documents of the Seville Cathedral, was employed to illuminate choir books during the mid 1430s.[3]

Parallels between the Rosenwald initials and those in Seville are wide-ranging and impressive.[4] Both show heavy ermine-lined drapery; closely comparable facial types (with long, parted beards); large, detailed hands; precisely drawn tile floors; the same repertoire of border and initial ornament; similar exploitation of the initials' spatial structure (e.g. the bar of the S becomes a table); and both are characterized by impressive series of prophet portraits.[5] On the other hand, the Rosenwald figures are fuller and more monumental, the structure and decoration of their initials is simpler, and, since all scenes are interiors not one includes a cypress tree. In fact, in conception and detail they are closer to the San Isidoro frescoes than to the Seville choir book initials thus far published. Whether the Rosenwald initials represent a stylistic phase of the Cypress Master himself or are the products of another illuminator within the Seville atelier, must await further research.

1. Diego Angulo Iñiguez, "El Maestro de los cipreses," *Archivo Español de arte y arqueologia 11* (May–Aug. 1928), passim. See also J. Domínguez Bordona, *Spanish illumination* (Florence 1930) vol. 2, p. 62, pl. 135, A–D.
2. Iñiguez, 1928, p. 92, pl. III.
3. Iñiguez, 1928, pp. 92ff.
4. Like the Rosenwald initials, those in Seville are nearly all square and measure c. 170–180 x 160–180 mm. See Iñiguez, 1928, p. 93n.
5. Iñiguez, 1928, pp. 72ff., pls. IV–VIII.

Fig. 46a. 1:1

A *(fig. 46a)* *Initial* S *with King David as Scribe*[6]
B-23,758
176 x 173 (6 15/16 x 6 13/16)
CONDITION (E) Colors very fresh with almost no rubbing or flaking; gold slightly tarnished; mounted on thick, white paper (as is whole set)

David, who holds a large reed pen, wears an ermine-lined red overgarment and a gold undergarment. The tiled floor is black and gold, and the furniture light brown. The double-headed dragon forming the initial is dark green, grayish blue, and rose.

172

Fig. 46b

B (*fig. 46b*, Colorplate x) *Initial T with a group of Benedictine monks singing before an altar from which issues water*
B-23,759
186 x 224 (7 3/8 x 8 13/16)
CONDITION (G/VG) Gold extensively flaked and rubbed; colors show occasional cracking and rubbing

The iconography of this initial is enigmatic. While scenes representing the performance of contemporary liturgical practices are not uncommon in initials of this type,[7] the lion-headed fountain on the altar and the bearded figure kneeling before it probably call for a historical or allegorical interpretation. If, as his facial type and garments might suggest, the figure is Saint Paul, the scene may allude to the "Water of Life" of the Christian faith.

More likely, it has been suggested the scene represents the local legend of Arles-sur-Tech (Pyrénées-Orientales, a late medieval pilgrimage site for northern Spain and southern France). A chapel in the Benedictine abbey of that town contained an early Christian sarcophagus with the bones of Saints Abdon and Sennen, out of which would miraculously flow pure water; and in special abundance on their Feast Day, July 30th.[8] The identity of the bearded figure remains to be explained.

Fig. 46c. 1:1

c *(fig. 46c)* *Initial* **N** *(?)* *with David in Prayer*
B-23,765
150 x 184 (5 7/8 x 7 1/4)
CONDITION (G) Extensively flaked and rubbed
　David, dressed in a red ermine-lined coat, kneels before a pink
architectural structure topped with green grass. Background tesserae
are gold and blue, floor tiles gold and black, and the dragon initial
grayish blue.

174

Fig. 46d. 1:1

D *(fig. 46d) Initial* I *with David*
B-23,766
152 x 115 (6 x 4 9/16)
CONDITION (E) Facial detail extremely well preserved; gold shows minor rubbing

David, dressed in a rose overgarment, grasps the grayish-green shaft of the initial.

Fig. 46e. 1:1

E *(fig. 46e)* *Initial* I *with David*
B-23,767
164 x 117 (6 1/2 x 4 5/8)
CONDITION (E)

David is dressed in an orange-red tunic beneath an ermine-lined
blue mantle. The bulk of the initial is rose

176

Fig. 46f. 1:1

F (*fig. 46f*) *Initial C with David (King Saul?)*
B-23,768
154 x 168 (6 1/16 x 6 11/16)
CONDITION (G) Face rubbed, gold flaked and rubbed
  This Old Testament King is seated on a red bed behind blue
curtains. His overgarment is dark grayish blue, his undergarment dark
green, and the initial is rose.

177

Fig. 46g. 1:1

G (*fig. 46g*) *Initial* L *with Old Testament prophet*
B-23,769
170 x 182 (6 5/8 x 7 1/8)
CONDITION (VG) Gold flaked and rubbed, some cracking of pigment
   This figure, dressed in a blue cloak and rose turban, is seated before a beige wooden table upon which are placed a scroll, book, a scrouge, two wooden boxes, and a ball of cord. The pointed gold object may be an implement for holding the cord while twisting it into rope, or perhaps the base of a candle stick. The curtains behind the figure are bright orange, the background dark brown.

178

Fig. 46h. 1:1

H (*fig. 46h*) *Initial D with David*
B-23,770
138 x 164 (5 1/2 x 6 7/16)
CONDITION (E) Gold only slightly flaked and rubbed; colors very
fresh; facial detail precise
   David, dressed in a dark grayish-blue garment and holding an
extended scroll, is seated on a gold pillow. The curtains on each side
are blue, those in the background bright red. The initial itself is rose,
with orange and dark green leafy extenders.

179

Fig. 46i. 1:1

1 (*fig. 46i*) *Initial* A
B-23,760
189 x 209 (7 1/2 x 8 1/4)
CONDITION (G/VG) Gold extensively flaked and rubbed
The five following non-figurative initials show color schemes includ-
ing rose, dark grayish blue, dark green, and bright orange red.

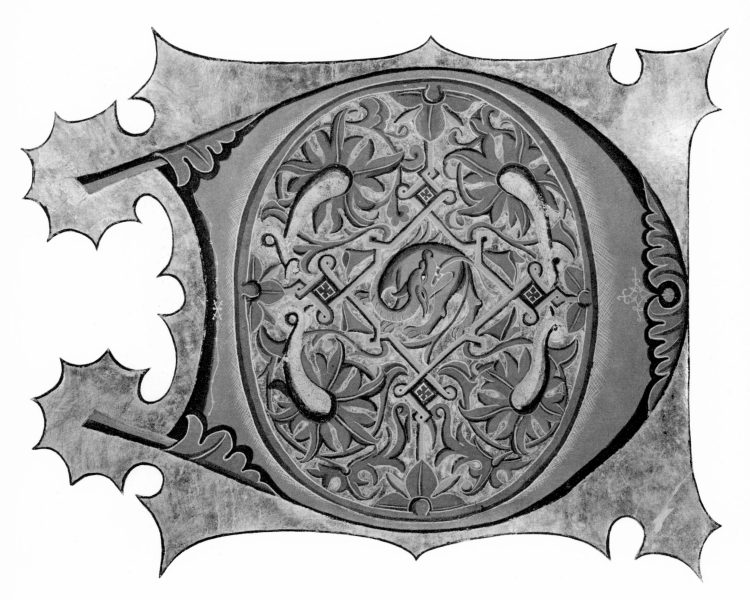

Fig. 46j

J (*fig. 46j*)   *Initial* D
B-23,761
170 x 215 (6 5/8 x 8 1/2)
CONDITION   (VG) Gold slightly cracked; minor flaking; pigments
fresh and bright

Fig. 46k. 1:1

K (*fig. 46k*)   *Initial* L
B-23,762
150 X 158 (5 7/8 x 6 1/4)
CONDITION   (VG) Only minor flaking; colors very fresh

182

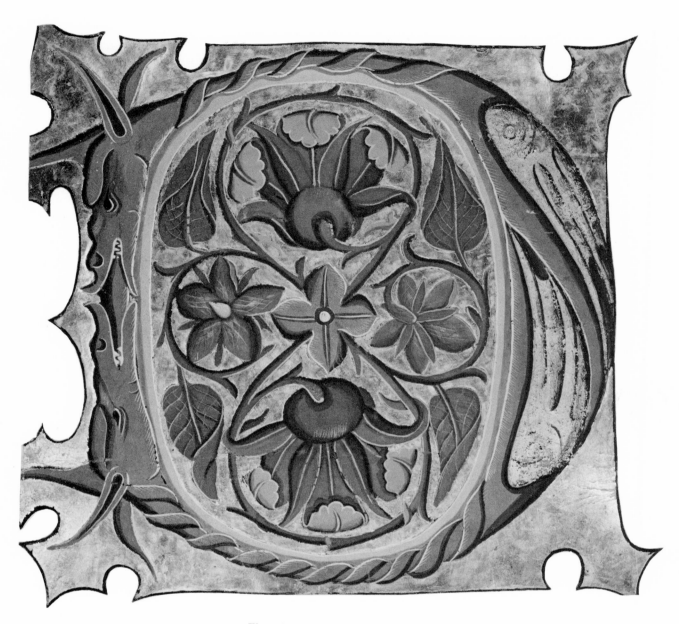

Fig. 46l. 1:1

L (*fig. 46l*)　*Initial* D
B-23,763
152 x 163 (6 x 6 7/16)
CONDITION　(G/VG) Gold rubbed; roughly trimmed

183

Fig. 46m. 1:1

M (*fig. 46m*)   *Initial* U (?)
B-23,764
177 X 191 (7 X 7 9/16)
CONDITION   (G)

6. The identification of the crowned figures in initials A, C–F, H as King David is based on their similarity to other initials from the workshop of the Master of the Cypresses wherein such figures are inscribed. See Iñiguez, 72ff., pls. IV–VIII. Antiphonaries from that workshop include extensive series of Old Testament prophets, among whom David took preeminence as author of the Psalms.

7. Iñiguez, 1928, pls. XV, D–XVI.

8. It is interesting to note that the diptych of the altarpiece shows companion portraits of two Saints, perhaps Abdon and Sennen. See Adolphe Crastre, *Histoire du martyre des saints Abdon et Sennen, de leurs reliques, de leurs miracles et de leur culte et de l'eau miraculeuse du sarcophage* (Perpignan 1910).

184

47

Miniature from a *Histoire Ancienne Jusqu'à César*

Meeting of Achilles and Hector
Flemish, mid-15th century
B-13,519
116 X 209   (4 9/16 X 8 1/4)

Middle French Gothic cursive script; 2 columns of 19 lines (incomplete) (c. 68 mm; and c. 155 mm wide)

CONDITION   (G/VG) Horizontal and vertical creases meet near center; border ornament severely rubbed; miniature well preserved

PROVENANCE   The Breton family of Tournemine; M. Capus, Cestayrols(?) (1894);[1] E. Warneck; A. Sambon; L. Rosenberg, Paris (1913); A. Sachs, New York (1930s); E. Rosenthal, Berkeley; L. J. Rosenwald, Jenkintown (1946); National Gallery of Art (1946)

EXHIBITED   Trenton, 1971, no. 40, illus.

BIBLIOGRAPHY   Seymour de Ricci, *Catalogue d'une collection de miniatures gothiques et persanes appartenant à Léonce Rosenberg* (Paris 1913), no. 27, pl. III; Brian Woledge, *Bibliographie des romans et nouvelles en prose Française antérieur à 1500 (Société de Publications Romanes et Française 42)* Geneva/Lille 1954), pl. 131

PARENT MANUSCRIPT   Location unknown: 109 folios (311 X 237 mm); 2 columns of 34 lines; 17 miniatures (12 leaves missing) (*fig. 47b*)[2]

RECTO   A prose version of Benoit de Sainte Maure's *Le roman de Troie* completed in 1264.[3] Although Woledge (see BIBLIOGRAPHY) terms our fragment "unidentified," it evidently comes from a copy of the second edition of a *Histoire ancienne jusqu'à César* (the first edition was compiled in 1206–1230), in which the fifth section of the original text was replaced by *Le roman de Troie* in a prose redaction:[4]

> COL. 1: *. . . guerre la et pres et loings ont ilz requis si long terme? Ja y auroit il assez de xv jours pour enterrer les mors? Oil certes, mais leur malicieux engin ne cognoist nulz, mais non pas pour tant trop seriot grant orgueil ce je desvouloye tout seul ce que plairoit a vous autres Sur ce ot dit maintes paroles ainçois que les truces fussent donnees; mais pource que moult estoient travailles tous les pluseurs si sont octoryees et li roy Priant l'afferma de sa partie III mois, a tant li messagés s'en tournerent a l'ost et Dolon les reconvoia par toute la force de la . . .*

> COL. 2: *et fu moult plus souef; si reposerent ceulx qui en orent la paine. Li Troyens ne finerent d'acroistre leurs murs et d'enforcier la ville. Si avint un jour que tous li roys et li princes grans dedans et dehors s'assemblerent. Li roy Priant et tous ses filz et ses barons d'une part, Agamenon et touz li princes de Grece de l'autre, pour aucunes choses que ilz se requirent, mais nulle requeste que li uns feist a l'autre ne fu celui jour menee a fin, fors celle du roy Thoas et d'Antenor que fu li uns quicte pour l'autre. Mais voir est que Calcas dont je vous ay parlé[5]. . . .*

VERSO (*fig. 47a*)   Continuation (after gap) of the recto text with the meeting of Achilles and Hector:

> COL. 1: *le menaça.*
> *Achilles ala veoir Hector li et sa compaignie et Hector et . . . . ent envers li et sa*

> COL. 2: *le tesmoignent que . . . . sont desmailliés par les coups de votre branc que maintes foiz c'est ja moliés en mon sange, si puis bien estre certain de mort, ce de vous ne me puis defendre que tant ce monstre votre cueur felon envers moy qu'il ne semble que vous aiez nul autre ennemy et moult avez donnez[6]*

Achilles and Hector, each with his entourage, meet in a meadow through which a stream, the Scamander, flows. The figures are

Fig. 47a. 1:1

dressed according to the courtly fashion of the mid-fifteenth century.

Their garments are blue (Hector and Achilles), light green, red, beige, and gold. Fine highlighting in gold is visible on the figure at the far left. The sky shades from dark blue toward white at the horizon; the grassy landscape is light green, and the border ornament blue, green, and gold.

This fragment was evidently once part of a copy of the second edition of *Histoire ancienne jusqu'à César*, sold through Sotheby in 1937.[7] The second edition exists in a number of fourteenth– and fifteenth–century manuscripts, at least two of which match our fragment in text and in the scene illustrated (Paris, Bibliothèque Nationale, cod. franc. 301, fols. 86v–87r; and cod. franc. 254, fols. 87v–88r).[8]

According to Professor Otto Pächt the style of courtly garments suggests a dating between 1440 and 1460. While the facial types and rather sketchy technique are reminiscent of the so-called Mansel Master, active apparently in the area of southern Belgium and northern France in the second quarter of the century,[9] the costumes and composition (large figures in the forward plane) recall the Girart Master, active at mid-century.[10] We know that the parent codex of the Rosenwald cutting was produced for a member of the Breton family of Tournemine, since their coat of arms (quarterly, gold and blue) appears in it on folio 61 verso.[11]

In a larger context, our leaf testifies to the program of Trojan studies undertaken at the courts of the Dukes of Burgundy and the

Fig. 47b. *Achilles playing chess in his tent and refusing to help the Greeks.* Location unknown (detail)

Kings of France, both of whom traced their lineage back to Aeneas. The subject of Troy was especially important to Philip the Good whose library contained seventeen volumes devoted solely to his family's descent from the Trojans.[12]

1. See the provenance given for our leaf's parent manuscript: Sotheby and Company, *Catalogue of Valuable Printed Books* . . . [Sale Catalogue: June 14–16, 1937] (London 1937), p. 102. We would like to thank Otto Pächt for bringing this manuscript to our attention.
2. Sotheby, 1937, lot 508, illus.
3. Benoit de Sainte Maure, *Le roman de Troie*, ed. Leopold Constans, 6 vols. (Paris 1912; reprinted: New York 1968), pp. 272ff. [PARENT MANUSCRIPT discussed, vol. 6, pp. 271ff.]
4. Woledge, 1954, 56ff. The leaf agrees word for word with fourteenth– and fifteenth–century copies of that text listed by Woledge.
5. Transcription is that of de Ricci (see BIBLIOGRAPHY).
6. The pledge of Hector and Achilles to engage in single combat is a complete departure from the tempestuous events of Book XXII of the *Iliad*. It shows the willingness of the medieval author to transform the classic text to conform with chivalric conduct.
7. See PARENT MANUSCRIPT and note 1.
8. The former is datable to the end of the fourteenth century; the latter to the second half of the fifteenth. For a list of such manuscripts see Woledge, 1954, 56ff.
9. Friedrich Winkler, *Die Flämische Buchmalerei des XV. und XVI. Jahrhunderts* (Leipzig 1925), p. 36, pls. 8–9.
10. Winkler, 1925, 41, esp. pl. 17.
11. Sotheby, 1937, p. 102.
12. See A. Bayot, *La Légende de Troie à la cour de Bourgogne* (Bruges 1908); G. Doutrepont, *La Littérature Française à la cour des Ducs de Bourgogne* (Paris 1909); and G. Caspar and F. Lyna, *Philippe Le Bon et ses beaux livres* (Brussels 1944).

48

Miniature from a Missal

Crucifixion
Lower Rhenish, later 15th
century
B-15,388
262 X 179   (10 3/8 X 7)

CONDITION   (G/VG) Miniature shows rubbing and flaking throughout; green (lower third of miniature) moderately deteriorated; the silver border squares have tarnished; pentimenti visible behind Christ; leaf trimmed all around
PROVENANCE   J. Rosenthal, Munich; E. Rosenthal, Berkeley; L. J. Rosenwald, Jenkintown (1949); National Gallery of Art (1949)
EXHIBITED   Munich, 1931, no. 33; National Gallery, 1950, no. 14, illus.; Los Angeles, 1953–1954, no. 76, illus.
RECTO (?)   Blank
VERSO (?) *(fig. 48a)*   The pale body of Christ, suspended before a light brown cross, emanates a delicate series of rays, tooled in the gold background. The Virgin wears a dark blue mantle over a pale pink tunic, while John is dressed in pale pink over greenish blue. The green earth of Golgotha is separated from the gold background by a broad strip of uncolored vellum. The border is alternately blue-black and very pale cream pink (the floral design of the latter being barely visible); the ornamental squares are alternately gold and silver.

This miniature was probably cut from a Missal, where it characteristically would have faced the *Te igitur* (Wherefore, we humbly pray and beseech Thee . . .) marking the beginning of the Canon of the mass.[1] Its format (including a broad rectangular border, ornamented in strips of delicate rinceaux separated by gold and silver squares); and its small, graceful figure of Christ and broad figures of the Virgin and Saint John (with half-closed eyes and unmodeled faces), recall a series of Crucifixion miniatures produced in Utrecht during the fifteenth century, one of the earliest of which (c. 1420) is found in a Missal in Haaren (Bibliotheek van het Groot-Seminarie).[2]

In spite of such general similarities an attribution to a specific Utrecht atelier is not possible. Instead, Dr. Friedrich Gorissen has suggested parallels with Lower Rhenish painting and sculpture of the later fifteenth century, citing several indicative motifs.[3] According to Dr. Gorissen, the earliest parallel for the motif of John's stiff collar is to be found in the Werner Willmering Crucifixion of 1458 in Cologne;[4] while the motif of the Virgin holding a length of her veil to dry her tears is taken up by Lower Rhenish sculptors around 1500. Furthermore, the free-floating loin cloth of Christ, drawn between His thighs, suggests a later fifteenth-century dating. Finally, Dr. Gorissen has pointed out that the repeated fold patterns on the Virgin's right arm and John's mantle show exact parallels among Cleve sculpture of c. 1475 and later, while counterparts for the Virgin's head type are found there toward the end of the century.

1. Comparable fifteenth-century Dutch "Canon pictures" are framed by broad fields of finely drawn border ornament. See Alexander Byvanck and G. H. Hoogewerff, *La Miniature Hollandaise dans les manuscrits des 14e, 15e, et 16e siècles* (The Hague 1922), vol. 2, pl. 189.
2. Byvanck and Hoogewerff, 1922, text vol., no. 16, fig. 12. Compare also Bruges, Musée Saint-Sauveur, fol. 7v [Byvanck and Hoogewerff, 1922, text vol., fig. 67 ("Utrecht before 1450")]; Utrecht, Universiteitsbibliotheek, cod. 402, fol 179v [Byvanck and Hoogewerff, 1922, vol. 2, pl. 189 ("Utrecht c. 1450")]. Also similar is the figure of Christ crucified in a Book of Hours: Leiden, Universiteitsbibliotheek, cod. B.P.L. 224, fol. 13v [see Byvanck and Hoogewerff, 1922, vol. 1, pl. 87 ("Utrecht c. 1440")].
3. We would like to thank Dr. Gorissen for sharing his knowledge of this period with us in a letter of August 12, 1974. See *Herbst des Mittelalters: Spätgotik in Köln und am Niederrhein* (Cologne: Kunsthalle, 1970), esp. Dr. Gorissen's introduction ("Künstler im Niederrheinland"; pp. 27ff.) and Heribert Meurer's essay on manuscript illumination (pp. 75f.).
4. Wallraf-Richartz-Museum, no. 88. See Herbert Reiners, *Die Kölner Malerschule* (M. Gladbach 1925), fig. 109.

Fig. 48a. 1:1

49

Miniature from a Book of
Hours (?)

Resurrection
Flemish (Bruges), c. 1530,
Simon Bening

B-22,897

70 X 48   (2 3/4 X 1 7/8)

Fig. 49b. Verso (?), 1:1

Spanish minuscule script; 18 lines (incomplete) (rule: c. 4
mm) (column c. 50 mm wide)

CONDITION   (VG) Pigment of flesh areas of Christ has deteriorated;
pigment flaked in lower left; trimmed all around; formerly pasted to
a heavy paper backing, now backed by thin vellum support

PROVENANCE   W. Sterling, 1849 (penciled notation inside cover of
former binding: "I bought these [14] cuttings [for the other 13 see
cat. 46] from a Spanish '*Libros Deloro*' at Madrid in 1849. W.S.");
B. Rosenthal, New York; L. J. Rosenwald, Jenkintown (1960);
National Gallery of Art (1964)

EXHIBITED   South Bend, 1972, no. 15

RECTO (?) (*fig. 49a*)   Christ, draped in a bright red mantle, stands
before a light blue sarcophagus; a staff with banner in His left hand.
The four attendant soldiers, portrayed in various stages of awakening,
are dressed in contemporary garments of bright green and brown
(foreground), blue-gray and dark blue (at the rear). In the background, which shades from strong browns and greens in the middle
distance toward a muted blue at the back, one can distinguish the
Three Holy Women returning from Golgotha (upper left), and the
city of Jerusalem, with the Church of the Holy Sepulchre (center
right).

VERSO (?) (*fig. 49b*)   (faintly visible) 18 lines of an as yet unidentified text (Hours of the Cross?).

This tiny miniature is closely related to the style of Simon Bening,
a leading[1] Flemish illuminator of the first half of the sixteenth
century who counted among his patrons Charles V of Spain and the
Infante Don Fernando of Portugal.[2] Around a small core of firmly
dated and attributed works, extending from his pre-1520 participation
in the Grimani Breviary (Venice)[3] to two self-portrait miniatures
of 1558,[4] has been amassed a substantial oeuvre, including several
luxuriously illuminated prayer books.[5] The Rosenwald Resurrection
miniature lacks the grandiose conception and Renaissance accoutre-
ments to be found in some of Bening's production, including those
miniatures attributed to his hand in the Grimani Breviary and in the
Heures de Hennessy in Brussels (Bibliothèque Royale, cod. II.58).[6]
Instead, its delicate atmospheric effects, and intimate emotive
qualities bear comparison with some of the miniatures in the so-called
Golf Book (of Hours) in the British Museum (cod. add. 24,098);[7] a
single leaf formerly in the Grete Ring Collection, London;[8] and
several of the sixty-four miniatures in the Walters Art Gallery,
Baltimore (cod. W442), presently mounted in a quadriptych.[9]

The precise nature of our miniature's parent manuscript has yet to
be determined. Such a small fragment may have been excised from
the center of a complex framing device on a leaf within a small
Book of Hours, like that in the Pierpont Morgan Library (cod. M339)
attributed to Simon Bening.[10] Or, it may have been part of a series of
New Testament scenes like those (cited above) in Baltimore. A
final judgment is difficult since Bening's miniatures were in some
cases created, and in many cases bought and sold, as small
independent devotional paintings.[11]

1. For Bening's wide reputation in his own day see W. H. James Weale, "Simon
Bennink, Miniaturist," *The Burlington Magazine 8* (Oct. 1905–March 1906),
pp. 355f.

Fig. 49a. 1 : 1

2. Friedrich Winkler, *Die Flämische Buchmalerei des XV. und XVI. Jahrhunderts* (Leipzig 1925), pp. 139f., pls. 80–88; Paul Durrieu, *La Miniature Flamande au temps de la cour de Bourgogne (1415–1530)* (Brussels 1921), pp. 37f., pls. LXXXVII, 4–XCII. Professor Otto Pächt kindly shared his special knowledge of Simon Bening with us.

3. Paul Wescher, "Sanders and Simon Bening and Gerard Horenbout," *Art Quarterly 9, no. 3* (Summer 1946), 197, 204, fig. 17; Winkler, 1925, pl. 86, b–d.

4. One is in the Victoria and Albert Museum, London, and the other was formerly in the Lehman Collection, New York. See Wescher, 1946, 208; Durrieu, 1921, pl. LXXXVII, 4 (London); Weale, 1906, illus. p. 356 (formerly New York).

5. For a list see Winkler, 1925, 140.

6. Durrieu, 1921, pl. LXXXIX.

7. Compare especially Winkler, 1925, pl. 82, 1. Also similar are the miniatures in another Book of Hours in the British Museum (cod. Egerton 2125). See Winkler, 1925, pl. 82, 4.

8. Paul Wescher, "Beiträge zu Sanders und Simon Bening und Gerard Horenbout," *Festschrift Friedrich Winkler* (Berlin 1959), fig. 9.

9. Baltimore, 1949, no. 212, illus.

10. Belle da Costa Greene and Meta P. Harrsen, *The Pierpont Morgan Library: Exhibition of Illuminated Manuscripts* (New York: New York Public Library, 1933–1934), no. 132, pl. 89. See also Wescher, 1959, figs. 3, 5, 8, 11. The Rosenwald miniature closely corresponds in size and style to three cuttings (67–69 mm high) sold through Graupe in 1930 and attributed by Winkler (1925, 140, 160) to Simon Bening. See Hermann Ball and Paule Graupe, *Eine Wiener Sammlung, 2* [Sale Catalogue: May 12, 1930] (Berlin 1930), lots 20–22, illus. Winkler suggests that the five New Testament episodes on the three cuttings may have been excised from a Book of Hours, several full leaves of which were formerly in the Paris collection of Comte Durrieu (Durrieu, 1921, pl. XCII).

11. Winkler, 1925, 139; Wescher, 1946, 208.

Indices

Concordance

Accession Number	Catalogue Number	Census Number [1]
B-LJR	24	—
B-13,512	44	3
B-13,516	37B	6
B-13,517	37A	7
B-13,519	47	12
B-13,520	39	15
B-13,521	33	—
B-13,522	3	4
B-13,523	10	8
B-13,524	23	13
B-13,659	17	1
B-14,049	32	10
B-14,835	40A	20
B-14,836	40B	20
B-14,837	40D	20
B-14,838	40C	20
B-14,842	21	16
B-14,843	30	11
B-14,851	20	9
B-14,961	14	17
B-14,986	9B	18
B-14,987	9A	19
B-15,386	45	25
B-15,388	48	26
B-15,390	38	21
B-15,391	35	14
B-15,392	16	34
B-15,393	7	—
B-15,394	12	22
B-15,395	22	23
B-15,886	4	30
B-15,887	13	29
B-17,714	1	31
B-17,715	27	32
B-18,752	43	35
B-18,753	41C	36
B-18,754	19	34
B-18,755	41A	38
B-18,756	41B	44
B-18,757	31	33
B-18,760	5	—
B-18,761	18	41

1. Christopher U. Faye and William H. Bond, *Supplement to the Census of Medieval and Renaissance Manuscripts in the United States and Canada* (New York, 1962), pp. 126ff.

B-20,651	6	43
B-21,292	36	42
B-21,963	11	—
B-22,018	28	47
B-22,128	8	28
B-22,223	26	—
B-22,224	34	—
B-22,225	15	—
B-22,895	42	37
B-22,897	49	—
B-22,908	29B	—
B-22,909	29A	—
B-22,919	2B	—
B-22,920	2A	—
B-22,921	25	
B-23,758 to B-23,770	46A–M	—

Index of Artists